AN ART THERAPIST'S VIEW OF MASS MURDERS, VIOLENCE, AND MENTAL ILLNESS

"Andrea Yates"

Figure 1. On June 20, 2001, wanting to send them to a better place—heaven—Andrea Yates drowned her five children in the bathtub. She had attempted suicide previously and suffered from post-partum depression and post-partum psychosis. Nevertheless, she was left alone in the house with the children. Yates was convicted of capital murder and sentenced to life in prison. The verdict was overturned on appeal and she was found innocent by reason of insanity. She is serving her sentence in a state mental institution in Texas.

AN ART THERAPIST'S VIEW OF MASS MURDERS, VIOLENCE, AND MENTAL ILLNESS

Practical Suggestions for Helping Practitioners Find Support and Guidance in a Dangerous Practice

By

MAXINE BOROWSKY JUNGE

CHARLES C THOMAS • PUBLISHER, LTD.
Springfield • Illinois • U.S.A.

Published and Distributed Throughout the World by

CHARLES C THOMAS • PUBLISHER, LTD.
2600 South First Street
Springfield, Illinois 62704

© 2019 by CHARLES C THOMAS • PUBLISHER, LTD.

ISBN 978-0-398-09277-1 (paper)
ISBN 978-0-398-09278-8 (ebook)

Library of Congress Catalog Card Number: 2019008671 (print)
2019017851 (ebook)

Printed in the United States of America
MM-C-1

Library of Congress Cataloging-in-Publication Data

Names: Junge, Maxine Borowsky, author.
Title: An art therapist's view of mass murders, violence, and mental illness
    : practical suggestions for helping practitioners find support and
    guidance in a dangerous practice / by Maxine Borowsky Junge.
Description: Springfield, Illinois, U.S.A. : Charles C Thomas, Publisher,
    LTD., 2019. | Includes bibliographical references and index.
Identifiers: LCCN 2019008671 (print) | LCCN 2019017851 (ebook) | ISBN
    9780398092788 (ebook) | ISBN 9780398092771 (paper)
Subjects: LCSH: Art therapists--Professional ethics. | Art therapy. |
    Murder--Psychological aspects. | Violence--Psychological aspects. | Mental
    illness--Psychological aspects.
Classification: LCC RC489.A72 (ebook) | LCC RC489.A72 J86 2019 (print) | DDC
    616.89/1656--dc23
LC record available at https://lccn.loc.gov/2019008671

This book is for those who stand up for what is right.

And for my children Benjamin and Alexa, who do.

ALSO BY MAXINE BOROWSKY JUNGE

A History of Art Therapy in the United States

Creative Realities: The Search for Meanings

Architects of Art Therapy: Memoirs and Life Stories
(with Harriet Wadeson)

Mourning, Memory and Life Itself: Essays by an Art Therapist

The Modern History of Art Therapy in the United States

Graphic Facilitation and Art Therapy,
Imagery and Metaphor in Organizational Development
(with Michelle Winkel)

Identity and Art Therapy: Personal and Professional Perspectives

Becoming an Art Therapist
(with Kim Newall)

Voices from the Barrio
"Con Safos: Reflections of Life in the Barrio"

Dear Myra, Dear Max
A Conversation About Aging
(with Myra Levick)

I once read that the root of all anger is fear, particularly a fear of those things we cannot control.

—Brittany Cooper, *Eloquent Rage*

Ours is essentially a tragic age, so we refuse to take it tragically. The cataclysm has happened, we are among the ruins, we start to build up new little habitats, to have new little hopes. It is rather hard work: there is now no smooth road to the future: but we go around, or scramble over the obstacles. We've got to live, no matter how many skies have fallen.

—D. H. Lawrence

When people conclude that all is futile, then the absurd becomes the norm.

—Stanley Crouch

PREFACE

There have been times when I thought I should title this book *Everything I've Ever Wanted to Say About Everything.* Writing it has given me the opportunity to revisit and reconsider my deepest source—my history as an art psychotherapist in a variety of clinical settings and in teaching. Exploring through writing, I have remembered again valiant struggles of students and colleagues to help the clients they serve as bureaucracy has burgeoned and encroached deliberately. I have watched them hold onto their humanity grimacing, unsung but bathed in light in what has always been a difficult and all-too-often inhuman mental health system. I admire their bravery. Sometimes simply continuing on is an act of courage.

Formally, I became a clinical art psychotherapist and teacher in the early 1970s just as the mental health system was dramatically changed. My history in the art therapy field coincides with the history of modern mental health. Originally thought to be a major advance over the old days, as in most things, unsettling problems have emerged. Unfortunately, the struggle is not ended. It has simply become more complicated. I believe it has gotten worse for clients and for clinicians who carry on together with hope despite inherent dangers and despite immeasurable obstacles. In this book you will find my thoughts on a variety of issues of creativity, violence and mental illness, framed around the phenomenon of mass murders. Most have been turned over, inside out and crafted in conversations over the years with students, colleagues and friends in my living room in front of the fireplace They are the ideas of an art psychotherapist who has been active in the mental health system for almost fifty years.

In the 1970s, when I first began clinical practice, a colleague's house was burned down by a client she was seeing in an outpatient clinic. Her baby was saved—they threw him out the window—but her husband died in the fire. She was very badly scarred and terrifically shaken. It was a horrifying wake-up call for me about the dangers people who engage with mental illness may encounter. I never forgot it. It remained an unforgettable, ever-present memory and in a myriad of ways, this book, more than forty-five years later, is the result.

M.B.J.

ACKNOWLEDGMENTS

I have worked with my publisher Michael Thomas at Charles C Thomas Publishers for 18 years in a literary partnership and I want to thank him and his staff for their support and appreciation of my work and for being endlessly helpful. Most importantly to me, they have been non-intrusive, perfect for the way I work. I have never met Michael in person but have had a long email relationship with him where we discussed and argued about punctuation (he was generally right) and wrote about our families, as our children grew up and expanded into their own lives. As an artist, I am particularly picky about visual imagery and thus am exceedingly grateful to Trevor Ollech who created the spectacular cover designs for many of my books—often using my own artwork.

Diane Divelbess encouraged me to thank my familiar old desk chair, with me for 40 years, traveling from Los Angeles to Whidbey Island and supporting me (so to speak) through the writing of my dissertation, books, articles and a variety of other things. In the middle of writing this book, it finally had enough and went to the dump. I am just getting to know my new desk chair and hope it can be as effective as my old.

My wonderful house has sheltered me and my curiosity, helped me clean out the cobwebs, given me a sweet place for dreaming and nurtured my writing and art for 18 years. I will miss it.

I thank Catherine Robinson for everything.

David Wilder offered an appreciative listening ear and important documents. In the course of writing, he also put up some motion lights on my house. I am grateful to him for the many roles he plays in my life.

Betsy, my Havanese dog, slept quietly, snoring on her rug underneath my computer, while I wrote. Her furry and comforting presence contributed in many ways.

My son, Dr. Benjamin Junge is my computer/tech consultant. Technological ninny that I am, I call on him for help where ever he is in the world. (For the last six months, he has been in Brazil.) I am grateful for his good-hearted willingness to help, despite his own heavy research and teaching demands. Our weekly discussions provided me with an intellectual scholarly colleague who is thoughtful, imaginative and knowledgeable. Ben took the pictures of my artwork for this volume.

My fabulous daughter Alexa's caring, understanding and interest in her mother's peculiar obsession has meant everything.

Much of the research and thinking for this book was done at the John Auburn's Whidbey Island Bagel Factory in Clinton. I walk in the door and am handed my cup of coffee and my bagel is automatically inserted into the toaster. When I came to Whidbey 18 years ago, I made the bagel shop my office. I want to thank John and his staff for making it more than an office and treating me like family.

My work on mass murders and keeping therapists safe, culminating in this book, has been a long process. But not everyone I talked to about the project was enthusiastic. Many felt the subject too horrifying and best avoided. However, there were some. For their support and ideas, I acknowledge the essential role played by those who have come in and out of my life over email and in person during that time—students, mentees and friends at Antioch University in Seattle, in Los Angeles and on Whidbey Island, Washington. Ellen Stewart, Danna Rooth and Katie Kapugi's enthusiasm for the urgency of safety for art therapists has provided incentive when my own might have lagged.

CONTENTS

AN ART THERAPIST'S VIEW OF MASS MURDERS, VIOLENCE, AND MENTAL ILLNESS

Chapter 1

INTRODUCTION

Writing is done in solitude but it is by no means made in isolation. In that solitude I find the quiet to think and respond to the world and the things people have said, and everything I write is in conversation with others.

—Rebecca Solnit, *Call Them by Their True Names*

My interest in the human personality's mysterious intersection of violence and mental illness has been present for decades—in all the years of my formal career as I practiced clinical art psychotherapy and directed a Master's-level graduate training program in Clinical Art Therapy and Marital and Family Therapy, first at Immaculate Heart College and then at Loyola Marymount University in Los Angeles. In those over-busy days, I had little time to make my own art. When I retired from LMU and moved to Whidbey Island, 18 years ago, I stopped active involvement with clients and finally had time and energy to make my own artwork. I moved from a practicing art therapy clinician and took up again my persona as a visual artist who had been waiting in the wings all that time. Fascinated before now as a practicing art therapist, I remained intrigued with how the human personality could manifest a congruence of mental illness and violent aggressive behavior and decided to focus my artwork there. On Whidbey Island, I painted and drew about mass murders (which unfortunately kept coming in real life). My paintings and drawings are included in this book in Chapter 5.

This volume is not about terrorist killings or killers. As achingly horrifying and terrible as it is, a terrorist killing can be explained on political terms. A mass murder without terrorist intentions is, I think, ultimately unexplainable. It is a complicated, yet pared away, articulation of the human personality, and all-too rampant these days.

Motives may actually differ but mental illness is often a suspected cause of mass murders and the broken mental health system readily accused. For the purposes of this book "mass murder" is defined as one in which more than one person is killed at one time. Both Andrea Yates who drowned her five children in the bathtub to give them a better life in Heaven and Dylann Roof who killed nine African Americans at the Emanuel African Methodist Episcopal Church in Charlotte, North Carolina in 2015 with white supremacist motivations are mass murderers. Mass murder is contrasted to "serial killing" where the killer kills one person and then another and another etc., at a later time.

There has always existed unsettling disruptive behavior by people with mental illness. Many rightly or wrongly diagnosed with mental dysfunction spent their lives institutionalized in asylums or, since the 1960s, in jails. During the Kennedy years (1960s,) despite indisputably good intentions a sea change occurred in the treatment of mental illness. It was the effort to end the psychiatric "warehousing" of people, many of whom spent decades in institutions (cf. Chapter 4, Martin Ramirez). The focus was to empty out the state mental institutions and treat the unwell in community mental health centers in their home neighborhoods. Nothing is simple, however and as always, there were unforeseen ramifications. Later, politicians, such as Ronald Reagan, Governor of California and then United States President slashed funding and all but closed existing psychiatric hospitals, leaving very few beds for the seriously ill. Known as "deinstitutionalization," this major shift, broadly and visibly, moved people with mental dysfunctions into communities—particularly cities, expanding and multiplying where financing for enough community treatment facilities and services failed to materialize. Many believe that the ever-broadening phenomenon of urban homelessness is the direct result of deinstitutionalization and that jails have become vast holding cells for the mentally ill—especially black prisoners. Others with mental dysfunctions remain among us, where they have always been.

Let me be clear: I am not saying that *all* violent behavior is committed by people with mental illness. Nor am I saying that people with mental illness are necessarily violent. What I *am* saying is that mental illness is probably *one cause* of violence, along with a variety of other things including poverty, substance abuse and the ready accessibility of guns that for many make the world fearful and unsafe. For many the world appears to have slipped off its axis.

Some blame this feeling of unease on an increase in world population. Some blame it on the NRA[1] and the proliferation of guns and loose regulations in the United States. Some blame it on the ramifications of the technology blitz. Some blame it on video games and gamers. Some blame it on terrorists, homegrown and from abroad.[2] Whatever the realities, a generalized fear[3] along with a profound sense of anxiety, exhaustion, instability and unpredictability predominate human consciousness and are ubiquitous today in American life.

Another point: Although this book concerns mass murders, at times committed by people with mental illness, some of whom, like Andrea Yates, had long documented problematic histories, I am not saying, by definition, that mass murderers *are* mentally dysfunctional or diagnosable. Many people do believe exactly that. It *is* true that most mass murderers if not all, probably have some aberrant behavioral issues that could be classified as early warning signs of mental illness. Although serious mental illness, in a second, can change a calm, relatively reasonable person into a violent monster, mass murders are typically carefully planned over a period of time and are not due to what is called "snapping."

The search for a motivation for a mass murder usually begins immediately after the event and produces speculations, typically about the shooter's "mental illness," proclaimed as "facts" before any real facts are known. That there must be a discoverable motivation for such a terrible act is a virtual truism. Formulation and understanding of a motivating cause is the narrative story about the "prequel," the "why" to the heinous act. It seems important to find out and know, even though the relevant discovery of motivation may be partially true

---

1. The NRA, as most know, is the National Rifle Association, the major lobbyist for gun rights, based on the Second Amendment of the United States Constitution.
2. In 2017 *The Wiley Handbook of the Psychology of Mass Shootings* edited by Laura C. Wilson was published. It contains research articles on the subject (including politically-motivated terrorist shootings) by researchers, sociologists, criminalists and academics. Most of the research is on the aftermath and trauma of mass shootings, not on how to avoid or predict them. From what I can tell, this is the first book about psychology and mass killings to be published.
3. Journalist Bob Woodward's book has recently been published. With a portrait of U.S. President Trump on its red cover, it is named *Fear.* Woodward writes that when Trump was asked to define power, he said "fear"!

or altogether false because discovery of motivation is the well-intentioned attempt to make the unexplainable, explainable. If we can understand the motivation, then we can feel normal again and safe in our own skins.[4] If we know why (or even think we do), then we can feel comforted that we are *different* from the murderer and the world can tilt back on it's axis and anxiety subside. Common wisdom concludes: "who would do such a horrible thing unless they are crazy; therefore, logically, the person who did it must have a mental illness." This immediately leapt-to assumption is a psychological coping mechanism, a way of understanding evil acts which inherently are not understandable, making those who carry them out distant and different from "normal" people. Unfortunately, it is not that simple.

I believe in historical progress, but after almost 50 years of clinical psychotherapy and art therapy teaching and practice, despite our best efforts, I am convinced that human personality—it's motivations and actions—remain complex and thus far, largely mysterious and unknowable. The old iceberg story applies: We see a bit of it at the surface of the ocean, but there is a large and unknowable area beneath the surface that we cannot see and we cannot know which can sink even our most safe and enduring ships. We do our best with the information we can see, can learn and can know. As art therapists, we search for patterns, speculate, predict and treat, but our abilities to tolerate and work within the ambiguity and existential unknowability of the human condition is an important skill that an art therapist cannot do without. This is the pragmatic reality we live and work in. Like medicine, an art psychotherapy practice is an art, not a science. This has always been true and is true today. We wish it were science and predictable, but it's not!

Is a mass murder a crime or an act of a mentally ill person? To go to trial, a mass murderer must be declared sane. But even legal definitions of mental disease or insanity change and generally the only relevant question is "does the person know right from wrong," at best, a changing definition. One would hope advancement in thinking might result in a more accurate and improved definition. Unfortunately, not. Roth (2018) writes:

---

4. Recently, when a baggage handler stole a plane from SeaTac Airport, within two hours of the event and before any of the background information was known, I heard an "expert" speaking on TV giving a detailed story about the surrounding causation, including that the pilot was clearly suicidal and had been for a long time. Assumptions and hogwash!

. . . In biblical times and still today in some cultures, seeing visions or hearing voices is an indication of holiness, not madness. . . . Throughout our history we have struggled to figure out what transgressions should be considered crimes: for a brief period within my grandparents' life-times, it was against the law to drink a glass of wine; within my parents' life-time interracial marriage was illegal. In my adult life, I have watched marijuana become legal in state after state. (p. 4)

Diagnosing and treating mental illness is complicated with no definitive testing such as there is for physical disease. Mental illness cannot be diagnosed from a blood test! When I began clinical practice there was no *Diagnostic and Statistical Manual*[5] the therapist's diagnostic "Bible" today, developed to standardize, guide and define the thinking of clinicians and health insurance companies. Many mental health workers and others today consider the DSM "Truth." It is not. Over the years, definitions of diagnoses shift and move. Probably the most remembered story about the DSM is that in 1973 homosexuality was classified as a sexual deviance disorder—a pathology. Although it took 42 years, homosexuality as a pathological diagnosis was removed December 15, 2015. Sometimes a change is because of the advance of scientific information; more often, like this one, it is the result of sociopolitics.

Like every human creation, the DSM is only partially "true" at best. Dylann Roof, who killed nine black people at the Emanuel African Methodist Episcopal in Charleston in 2015, had no documented mental health history at all, had never seen a therapist, nor been diagnosed for anything and, as far as we know, had never behaved in any way vastly different from the norm. Assessed competent to stand trial, can it be said that white supremacist ideology is "crazy" and drives someone to kill? It is what motivated Roof, but

---

5. *The Diagnostic and Statistical Manual of Mental Disorders* I was first published in 1952 (and it was later than that that it was broadly used.) Before, there were a number of other mental health classification systems, but they were not widely used. The *DSM* was published by the American Psychiatric Association, the professional organization for M.D. psychiatrists. It has had five editions. The *DSM 5* is the first major revision in 20 years with significant changes to the categorization of schizophrenia. There are work groups of psychiatrists for each disorder, tasked with evolving definition and symptoms. In other words, the *DSM* intends to capture the best thinking it can about mental health and illness and has decided that *a committee* is the best way to do this. There are many who would question this central premise.

obviously it is not a mental illness diagnosis. White supremacy and racism are not psychiatric diagnoses in the DSM.

My curiosity about the life and personality of human beings is more compelling to me than fiction could ever be. My fascination with mysteries, patterns, puzzles and the complexities of the human condition was the main driver in my career as an art psychotherapist. Over decades I remained acutely attuned to and aware of the confluence of mental disturbance, violence and human personality. I continue to be fascinated to this day. Something in me? Perhaps. Unraveling and unsnarling the chaos so that, hopefully, it works better is the job—even the calling—of therapists. At its core, for many, it has something to do with trying to make a better world. As Jewish lore says it is a Jew's obligation to heal the world's wounds. In some small way, that has been central in my life.

Eighteen years ago, I moved to Whidbey Island, north of Seattle. As a visual artist since childhood with professional-level training, I reclaimed my artist Self. I discovered that my interests remained the same, as they had been when I was a practicing art psychotherapist—anger, violence, aggression wrapped within the human personality. But instead of working with therapy clients, I began making visual art about those same inner issues that continued to intrigue and mystify.

I noticed that some mass murderers had long and documented mental illness histories, even what we would call "red flags." I was curious about why these warning signs seemed to have been ignored, resulting in the final tragedy of murder. In my art, I created renditions of mass murders and mass murderers. I believe with painter Ben Shahn that form is the shape of content. My main interest was to make art that tried to pierce the depths of mental illness in the human condition and explored how, at times, it could result in mass murder. Edges of personality interested me, as they always had. As a westerner who lived her whole life by the ocean, I knew I liked living "on the edge" and believed with Hannah Arendt, that evil exists and is banal. I was intrigued by that stark metaphorical landscape where outliers live, the arid psychic land where people breach the boundaries of civility and cultural acceptance and can commit acts so heinous that they instantly become monsters. I was also interested in the nature of contemporary American culture which increasingly seemed a crucible to enhance, allow, provoke and protect violence so that anger of all kinds could flourish and transform into hot flames. It was an

American culture in which mass murders could be carried out apparently daily.

This book is *not* about terrorist mass murders. It is about the less explainable ones. Other writers in other books will consider those terrorist tragedies and their motivations. When I looked over the 15 years of my artwork, I found that it represented events where some perpetrators sometimes had a long and even documented mental illness history and where any mental health professional with open eyes and the right training might have been able to predict at least a *potential* for violence. For example, from my first painting, of Andrea Yates, the Texas woman who drowned her five children in the bathtub, I became aware that rather than a sudden out-of-the-blue event as it seemed, some—but not all, of the mass murder perpetrators like Yates, had years of documented and sometimes even classic histories of severe mental dysfunction that had been ignored.[6] Why? Of course, it's easy in hindsight, the ticking time bomb element becomes all too evident. In hindsight, we can always know more clearly.

In my own art-making process, I intentionally and consciously kept my art therapist part—the psychologist, the interpreter and the critic—compartmentalized and tried to allow the artist in me a free rein. To start, I usually researched what information I could find about the murder event itself. I didn't plan the artwork and I didn't question what imagery appeared, nor it's meaning; over the years, my artwork has become expressionist in style. As mass murders increasingly occurred in American life, they continued to capture my interest. Photos of these drawings and paintings, along with descriptions of the specific occurrence are in Chapter 5 of this book.

The book's Preface describes the horrible event that taught me that psychotherapy is a dangerous profession. In Chapter 1, "Introduction," I set a stage for this exploration of mass murders, violence, creativity and mental illness. Chapter 2, "Laying out the context" concerns the contemporary societal and cultural landscape within which mass murders exist and increase. Chapter 3 "What we know now about mass murders and mental illness" is a brief history of the treatment of violence in mental health in the United States. Chapter 4 "Art, violence and mental illness" describes historic artistic figures in which violence and/or mental illness was an issue, including Hitler as an artist, the art

6. It is clear that Andrea Yates suffered from severe post-partum depression and psychosis.

of serial killers, the psychiatrically institutionalized artist Martin Ramirez and the Outsider artist Henry Darger. I also describe my own experience as an Expert Witness in the trial of serial killer Eric Leonard who shot six people. A discussion of the relationship of creativity and violence begins the chapter. Chapter 5 "Author's mass murder artwork" contains mass murders artwork with a brief description of each event. Chapter 6 "Some mass murders in the United States, October 2017-September 2018" are descriptions of mass murders which occurred during a year of the writing of this book. Chapter 7 "Why have we forgotten that children suffer? A reaction to the Marjorie Stone Douglas school shooting" is an essay evoked by the Parkland School shooting. Chapter 8 is "What can the art therapist do? Practical suggestions for helping art Therapists Find Help and Support in a Dangerous Practice I: Safety." Chapter 9 is "What can the art therapist do? Practical suggestions for helping art therapists find help and support in a dangerous practice and culture II: Applications." Chapter 10 is "Final comments: Darger and the calling of art therapy."

Chapter 2

LAYING THE CULTURAL CONTEXT

The Obama Years

Barak Obama's candidacy for United States President pierced the national citizenry's apathy born from the despairing grey haze of cynicism and revealed an unrealistic and naive, but still abiding hope, for a positive future and change. Obama's election in 2008 and his inauguration January 20, 2009 as the 44th and first African-American President created big expectations and eventually and inevitably, big disappointment. The AIDS pandemic had moved from being an acutely fatal disease to a chronic one because of protease inhibitors. With Obama's election, America erroneously congratulated itself on being "post-racial." Many thought that racism in the United States was finally over and, with Obama, the country would move forward.

After the profound national trauma of 9/11, America endured a long and apparently unwinnable war in a faraway land in which Americans died in numbers. When Obama took over the Presidency, he inherited from the previous administration of George W. Bush, not the hoped-for open landscape on which to etch a better future, but grave and immediate economic difficulties which threatened to sink America within an economic depression it hadn't seen the likes of in years.

Obama managed to save the economy, but many of his intended and hoped-for social changes had to be put aside. All-too-often, his slogan of "Yes we can!" became "But we couldn't." During the Bush and Obama years, many Americans' houses and jobs disappeared. Inequality rose—the poor got poorer and the rich got richer—and serious pervasive social problems persisted and spread. Racism flourished.

Erosion of the American Dream

I first noticed what I defined as the erosion of the "American Dream" in the late 1970s and early 1980s when American young people stopped being able to get jobs and because they could not afford to support themselves separately often went home to live with their parents. This was a huge psychological shift in the American psyche, ethos and zeitgeist but as far as I could tell, it went largely unseen then. There was no bellowing Paul Revere galloping through the streets to alert the citizenry to changes already on their doorstep and to come. With promise and hope as a reflection of American optimism and positivity, by Obama's time, for many, the potential and reality of an "American Dream" and the previously natural progression of the idea of "with hard work doing better than your parents," had reached a level of impossibility and hopelessness. Despair took root. Do better than your parents? Grown children were often not able to find a paying job, much less buy a house. They moved home in droves, took unpaid internships and counted themselves lucky.

Tech Revolution and the Changing Nature of Work

Twenty-first century technological innovations came along so fast that human adaptation to them became all but impossible—there simply wasn't the time to get used to it all. The internet, social media and the digital age infected and excited the population with speed, multi-tasking and meaningless filler. It became unusual for people to actually talk to each other or even look at each other. Instead, they looked down at their phones and texted—sometimes to the person sitting next to them. The family dinner became a thing of the past. Hard surfaced contemporary restaurants had a constant high level of noise. Conversation all but ceased. Eat fast and move on became the message. With the push of a button, a vile message could be sent anonymously.

The nature of work changed. Automation caused many to lose traditional jobs and were supplanted when possible with low-pay or part-time ones. Workers' safety nets—benefits—largely disappeared as did retirement pensions. Entitlement programs were threatened. While younger generations couldn't find work in this climate, olders were often fired to make way for younger, and cheaper workers.

During this time, the legal practice of "affirmative action" in universities and colleges admissions processes was all but abolished. Although race and ethnicity "balancing" remained for awhile, it was constantly threatened as a form of discrimination and white applicants were often beneficiaries.[1] On TV, zombie shows emerged enabling a visual form of aggression, decay and death to be visible, but always with the comfortable reassurance that "they" are different from us.

"Have a Nice Day" and "Move On"

During the Trump era, there was no time to listen or to contemplate much of anything. We were too busy with the intricacies of getting through life as it had come to be lived. Voices of philosophers and scholars of the meta-message were lost in the onslaught. From this roiling, uncontrollable, difficult underlying day-to-day reality, at the surface of life, a repressive "have a nice day" culture dominated. "Moving on" became a catchword and a codeword. It meant: don't let yourself get bogged down in the muck of anything. Keep moving. Avoid suffering. Don't stop to feel any pain. Don't stop at all! If you keep moving fast enough you may not see the detritus beneath your feet, chasing you, attempting to overwhelm your life.

Amidst President Donald Trump's rawness, lack of civility and cruelty, what it meant to be poor and what it meant to be rich increasingly became more distant. U.S. politics became extreme conservatism and looked to a remembered past as the ideal. Confrontation became a dirty word and in many quarters, especially after Trump was elected, any form of rational debate ceased as it was sure to elicit uncontrollable rage. In the land of Capitalism, Americans who could, and who had the money, were able to pretty much live within a life-as-usual bubble. Many were not so lucky. Bubblers included many white people, most well-intentioned of course, but few consciously aware of their inherent privilege and what it meant.

Forgiveness

After Dylann Roof's massacre of nine in the Charleston church, the concept of "forgiveness," a plank of Christian values became more pronounced. As a national concept, it fit right in with the "Move On" culture. Many of the Black members of the Charleston church in which

---

1. See the current legal doings against Harvard College in which the plaintiffs assert that current practices against Asian applicants are unconstitutional discrimination.

Dylann Roof shot and killed nine parishioners after praying with them in a Bible study class, forgave him as an act of Christian charity. Implicit in the act and motive of "forgiveness" is a letting go of the negative feelings and the anger one might feel about some small or huge slight—even a mass killing. It encompasses the notion that if a person (victim?) doesn't let go and forgive, *their anger comes back to bite THEM,* not the perpetrator of the crime. The idea is that holding onto anger destroys the victim. When the person lets go of the anger, through the act of forgiveness they can be clean again.[2]

Genuine letting go is a long and difficult psychological process. Despite the contemporary cultural edict, it is impossible to do it hastily. We are admonished to let go as quickly as if one is changing dirty socks. People are not really psychologically able to do this, even if they want to. Within this idea of forgiveness, a person is likely to push aside unacceptable feelings of rage and hate which may go underground deep within the human psyche.[3] There they remain smoldering, no longer "socially acceptable" or allowable. And the anger remains inexpressible in any way that might be a healthy and normal reaction to a sometimes huge wrong. Should Dylann Roof have been forgiven?

Lying and the Lack of Civility

In the Trump years, lying, unethical behavior, lack of integrity, "fake news" and designating the press as the "enemy of the people" became not only acceptable, but commended by many as the domain of "winning."[4] With Trump's advocacy, implicit and explicit calls to violence, overt racism, non-politically correct language, bullying, discrimination and demagoguery came out of the darkness where they had been sleeping, ready and with one eye open, and became not only permissible but openly admired by many. Plain old civility all but ceased, led by the example of a crude and cruel President often

---

2. Forgiveness is sometimes considered a necessity of survival for southern blacks.

3. This was called the psychological defense mechanisms of "sublimation" or "repression." Sublimation is thought to be conscious. Repression is unconscious.

4. As I write this book, many women are going public about their experiences of sexual harassment and abuse and the "Me too" and "Times up" movements have shown how widespread this experience is. But before that even, there were the Bill Cosby accusers and later a trial indicating that even an apparently nice man was prone to want to use his power over women. I believe that the courageous women who are speaking out are bringing into the light and making visible, a shadow side of American life that has always existed and was heretofore acceptable.

openly mocking the less powerful such as the disabled. If a great deal of money was made in the bargain, all the better.

The surprise election of Donald J. Trump interrupted the flawless and fixed positional self-congratulatory posture that had prevailed. In those years, despite Donald Trump's racist birther challenge to the legitimacy of Obama's presidency, that we could elect an African-American was taken to mean we now lived in a "Post Racist Society." Despite the gains of second-wave "Feminism," and a better-than-it-used-to-be prevalence of women, feminism was unsettlingly thought by many young women to have been a negative movement and a dirty word. In the 21st century many women refused to call themselves feminists at all. The fact that feminism stood for *equity* and that women's salaries were still lower than men's seemed lost. Women had achieved so much, "had come a long way baby." Many men and women said, that should be enough anyway.[5] Domestic violence and child abuse were more out in the open, but that violence in desperate lives continued to boldly and secretly exist in many quarters was hardly recognized.

Fear, Anger and Violence Escalates

There *is* an undeniable, prevalent and escalating sense of violence, fear and anger. But where does it go psychologically in the "Have a Nice Day" and "Move On" culture? How can we understand the juxtaposition of the cruelty and divisiveness of Donald Trump coexisting with a surface of kindness, comfortableness, inclusiveness and positivity—where Americans typically opened their hearts and donated huge amounts of money to disaster victims and others? In the Trump era of intense tribalism, neighbors continue to unselfishly help neighbors.

Where does the escalating sense of anger and violence go psychologically? What is not allowed to be expressed becomes grimly subversive—a vital and energetic universe underneath a false, pleasant surface. Invisible, it's malevolent threat grows like a cancer, spreading it's tentacles everywhere. Unseen and unrecognized under any radar, it

---

5. The backlash to current realities of sexual harassment and the "Me too" movement is yet to be seen in the culture, but will undoubtedly come into being. That "Feminism" actually meant *equity* for women was largely lost within the notion of Feminists as overly-aggressive women trying unreasonably to "get their way." Feminism implied a loss of power for men, particularly white men. Currently, a few books have been published about women's anger and rage. Although rage can create change it can also lead to destruction. Casey Cep in *The New Yorker* "writes: Anger [must be] tempered with reason to create change...Kavanaugh and Blasy Ford are the different faces of anger ("The rage of women assessed," *The New Yorker,* 10/15/2018, p. 86).

has more opportunity to grow. Unnoticed, it spreads, infects, and influences. From this secret world underneath, an angry presence periodically oozes through cracks to the surface; it burbles up out of the dark and pierces our comfortable bubble to cause fear, chaos and death. As in the horrors of 9/11, it usually takes awful, unexpected death, like mass murders, to remind that there still exists this thriving other world.

On the Surface: Clues to a Secret Underworld

Clues to a secret underworld are rampant on the surface of life. Disturbing memories arise of childhood abuse and trauma, particularly with women as victims. Trauma and abuse? It seems to have happened to everybody. Everybody's experienced it! Internationally, the Catholic priesthood, has come under a spotlight for years of secret molesting, abusing and covering it up.

During a period in the 1980s, like a latter day Salem witch hunt, people confessed to what seemed to be an epidemic of Satanic Cults in their towns. Centering around preschools and daycare facilities, personnel of day-care facilities were regularly accused of molesting their charges and holding satanic rituals with the children. Back then, even whole towns confessed. "Believe the children" was the motto even though the children were sometimes as young as three and as young children do, were known to fantasize or downright lie. As widespread nationally as this abuse phenomenon was thought to be, no evidence of mass abuse or Satanic cults was ever found anywhere. Mass hysteria? Maybe. But what did it mean about paranoia, fear and the lack of acceptance of anger as a "normal" emotion.

Diminishing Avenues for Expression of Aggression

Through the last ten years of the 20th century and into the 21st, the American population grew as American culture became more violent. Social avenues for the expression of "acceptable" aggression were closing down or were gone altogether. In video games, killing and acting-out became ubiquitous. Bullying in schools was recognized as a constant but what to do about it and how to stop it was not simple.[6] The global internet spread messages of hate as individuals impul-

---

6. U.S. President Donald Trump was often called a bully, while his wife, "the first lady" had as her cause stopping bullying! She also recently said she was the most bullied person in the world.

sively and with no apparent civil filter sent angry and bullying messages with breakneck speed across international boundaries. Schools had major troubles: Anonymous cyber bullying led to what seemed to be a virus of suicides by adolescents whose teenage suffering and depression sometimes grew into hopelessness. School recess which might have given children and teenagers some physical outlet for their emotions disappeared along with arts programs, where previously many difficult children had been able to find a tolerant home. Teachers who once might have put up with a boy wiggling in the classroom, did so no longer sending him off to be diagnosed and medicated. There were more diagnoses of Attention Deficit Hyperactive disorder (ADHD[7]) particularly among boys. This disorder, whether rightly or wrongly applied, was largely viewed as a disease of the brain and treated with medication. This put many medicated and sedated (but quiet) zombies in classrooms.

Guns, Drugs and Escaping Reality

Buying and carrying guns proliferated and Betsy De Vos, the Health and Human Services Secretary of the Trump administration said in her congressional confirmation hearing that guns in schools were acceptable. She is now proposing that federal funds be used to provide guns to school personnel. Guns are easily accessible and have become an increasing public health hazard. Since the killings of primary school children at Sandy Hook, gun regulation laws nationwide have actually become less stringent.

Drugs, heroin and other ways to escape are epidemic and deadly. Overdosing with drugs is common. Rehabilitation facilities, covered by health insurance grow. Opiod addiction is a national problem. That we live in a reality we need to escape, through suicide, drugs or other means sometimes seems understandable.

Anxiety

In 2016, Donald Trump's unexpected election as President and his subsequent actions led to a heightened sense of anxiety, fear and felt chaos in the populace. People struggled to keep their balance within what seemed to be the total loss of known and expected structures and

---

7. From the *Diagnostic and Statistical Manual of Mental Disorders (DSM-IV & V)* (1994 & 2013).

systems. A kind of cultural numbness and denial helped people cope and in many states, marijuana became legalized.

In the 21st century, cultural aggression and violence internalized and grew and together with less outlets for safe expression, burst any bounds it may have had. It spread rampantly out of control and became all-too-prevalent, an ugly new normalcy. Bureaucracy increased, efficiency shrank. Rational thought seemed to have become a thing of the past.

Widespread use of computers created a distant culture, based in robotic response. The telephone, long an instrument of human communication became automated and computerized. Some people asked "Am I talking to a human?" If human, she or he might laugh. A computer never does.

The Changed Language of Problem Solving

Problem solving disappeared and was renamed as "challenge" and this language change was embraced in the mental health community. To call something a "challenge" rather than a "problem" or an "obstacle" was intended to be a more neutral definition. A "challenge" implies something a person could go around, even overcome. A problem? Maybe not. But the meaning of the new language now placed the problem squarely within the individual person's arena to experience, solve and *to be accountable for*. It ignored the obvious impact of oppressive institutionalized systems and structures, beyond any person's ability to solve but that daily impacted them. When the word "challenge" is used, it does not allow for the recognition that some obstacles and problems *are institutional and systemic* in American culture and are not likely to be changed through individual personal impact. Faith in institutions, including government died as private citizens became more and more cynical. Tax loopholes allowed successful corporations to avoid taxes through private acts of philanthropy. Anthropologist David Graeber in his 2018 book *Bullshit Jobs* writes that almost 50 percent of people say their jobs are meaningless and insignificant.

And in Mental Health

In public mental health clinics and in private clinical practices, things grew even more difficult. Previously, seriously underfunded, now clinics and clinicians were overwhelmed with larger numbers of clients with desperate problems. No one saw a therapist these days for a simple problem of living; They could not afford it and thus they waited until their illness got severe and often intractable to seek help.

There was little appropriate, real psychological backup for therapists and clients alike and a serious dearth of accountability. Some decades ago—wrongly—cultural edicts and the mental health community laid the blame for the causation of children's psychological problems squarely on parents—the "nurture" theory. For example, In the years I began clinical practice, autism was thought to be caused by "refrigerator parents," those that emotionally neglected their child. By the 21st century, the pendulum had swung to the other extreme of "nature" and a belief in mental illness *as a disease* usually of the brain, best treated by behaviorism and medication.

Within an increasingly dangerous society, some took appropriate safety measures, but many rural and urban, clinics, institutions and staff providing mental health treatment to seriously ill people remained in the pervasive bubble of denial with an "it can't happen here" attitude. Not used to the rate of change in computers and communication, in globalization and in looming climate change problems, in the culture, as anxiety spread, a kind of passive dependency set in for many along with a feeling of being "duped" and ignored by the government. Meanwhile, formerly apathetic others grew more active, informed and resisted. It was a divisive and tumultuous time.

Denial as a Way to Carry On

Some mental health professionals and institutions apparently had a hard time acknowledging the difficult day-to-day realities of the culture and of the clients they treated. Even within contemporary realities, they were seemingly unable to become conscious and aware of any imminent or potential danger within in their own workplace. Does it take a large dose of denial in order to continue on? Must the art therapist or psychotherapist find a way to feel psychologically safe which, for many, includes denial of reality? It is my speculation that one's own sense of being safe has more to do with genetics and personal history than with actual realities. According to Friedman (2016) the difference between the increasing rate of change going on in American life and people's lagging ability to *adapt* to that change has enhanced anxiety in the populace.

And Mass Murders Keep Coming

The events of mass murder, once more rare and dispersed, increased and with the advent of terrorist mass murders became an everyday occurrence. In his book *Rampage Nation,* Klarevas (2016) cites 111 gun massacres in the last fifty years. He writes: "They are taking place with greater frequency with the sharpest increase in deaths occurring the past decade . . . specifically over one-third . . . that's a 160 percent increase over the last decade" (p. 71). If a person commits a mass murder, most say they are, by definition, "crazy": You've got to be crazy to do such a thing goes the common wisdom. It is immensely more complex and mysterious than that, depending on the complexities of human personality and behavior—things we still don't know a lot about.

The Theory of Sublimation of Aggression no Longer Holds

Freud's theory of sublimation as a mature defense mechanism is the transformation of inappropriate aggressive and violent impulses into socially acceptable ones. It was a mere 40 years ago, that sublimation was assumed to be a predictable result of effective mental health treatment and in art therapy, a major theorist Edith Kramer espoused this concept. As most art therapists know, art and the creative process were thought to be distinctly useful tools for sublimation. Typical is author Sylvia Ashton-Warner's 1986[8] statement which I remember as "If he can draw my house in flames, he will not burn it down." Overly optimistic and unrealistic in today's society.

Many art therapists, inspired by Kramer's theory, believed that aggressive impulses would be sublimated through art, thereby becoming more socially acceptable and appropriate. It was also believed that a future act of violence by a patient or client was unusual and could typically be predicted and that most, no matter how severe their mental dysfunction, would never become violent. Some mental health workers still believe this: I recently heard one quoted as saying "People with Post Traumatic Stress Disorder *never* become violent."[9] Considerable research has shown that this statement is simply wrong.

---

8. Ashton-Warner, S. (1986, First published in 1963). *Teacher.* New York: Simon & Schuster.
9. On the one hand, it is quite well known that people with PTSD often explode into violence. On the other hand, saying "never" is always hazardous.

1965 On: Major Changes in Mental Health Laws in America

What happened to the mental health laws during the last decades? In 1963, President John F. Kennedy, in an historic speech and with all good intentions for better care, described his expansive new program to end the hideous custodial care of those with mental illness "incarcerated" for years in asylums, psychiatric hospitals and other institutions. Introducing a dramatic shift of treatment focus and with, some say, the family example of his sister Rosemary who had been lobotomized, Kennedy aimed to develop adequate resources for the mentally dysfunctional to be treated in their home communities. The evolution of the anti-psychotic drug chlorpromazine (Thorazine,) widely believed to alleviate the symptoms of severe mental illness was a huge incentive and helped to make this possible. Federal legislative funding of Community Mental Health Agencies enhanced deinstitutionalization and the release of people "warehoused" in underfunded and often inadequate psychiatric hospitals into the community. Many had serious mental health problems. Deinstitutionalized, now they were visible on the streets.

In 1967, Ronald Regan became governor of California. (California was known to be an "advanced" state at the time.) With passage of the California Lanterman-Petris-Short Act and Regan, involuntary hospitalization in California virtually ended and state psychiatric hospitals gradually, and sometimes not so gradually, closed. Very few available inpatient beds remained. If a seriously mentally impaired person relapsed or needed hospitalization, it became all but impossible to hospitalize her or him involuntarily or any other way. As a result, outpatient mental health practitioners no longer had inpatient hospitalization as a protective, sometimes necessary resource for their clients unless, as I used to say "there was already blood on the steps."

In 1980, Republican Ronald Reagan was elected President of the United States. With the Republican-controlled Senate, he blocked legislation which would have refunded the Community Mental Health Centers and provided for additional community projects for mental illness and prevention and the community mental health movement died. Fifty years later, the unfortunate reality is underfunded, inadequate care, tremendous neglect and dramatically increased rates of community violence. Today, "a third of the homeless are seriously mentally ill, as are 20%[10] of those incarcerated, and public facilities are overrun by untreated individuals" (E. Fuller Torrey, 2014.)[11] Many mentally ill are in prisons.

Individual Versus Community Rights in Mental Health Systems

America likes to think of itself as a bastion of civil rights but the rights of the individual have always legally contended with those of the community. For many years now, due to a well-intentioned but dark legislative history, individual rights prevail. It was the American Civil Liberties Union (ACLU) that took on and won individual civil rights cases in the courts in the 60s, which gave individuals over 18 the right to refuse treatment. (No matter that someone in the throes of a psychotic episode is unlikely to think themselves crazy and therefore commit themselves voluntarily!) This right of refusal was often intended to mean the right to refuse medication but functionally, mental health became a system in which it is very difficult, often impossible, to institutionalize someone involuntarily.

Even if a prediction is able to be made about a person's potential violence which might result in his or her apprehension thereby averting deaths, the mental health laws do not generally allow for intervention unless the person agrees to it and do not come into play to detain a person until after a violent act has been committed. Thus we are doomed to miserable hindsight.

Before I became an art psychotherapist, I was a graduate student in Social Work at the University of Southern California. My first clinical internship assignment was in a new Community Mental Health Center, four flights up, by elevator, in a bank building. I was already aware of the drastic switch of focus in the new mental health legislation, the philosophy and intentions of which I applauded and supported. But I was also aware—this was about 1970—that even accessibility, literally, to this clinic and its services was difficult. To find the right door in the bank building was confusing to *me;* I wondered what it might be like for a confused mentally ill person even to be able *find* the clinic, much less make use of its services. Although I surely hoped

10. Roth (2018) counts the current percentage much higher—in some states as much as 50% and she calls jail "the largest psych ward in America" (p.39.)
11. Fuller Torrey (2014) wrote that Reagan didn't know much about mental illness; he confused it with communism.

for better, it seemed to me, even then, that the accessibility of community treatment to seriously mentally ill people, was a question. Later with a student colleague, I advocated for easier to access storefront and "walk-in" treatment centers, not a new idea at the time, in which the client could at least walk in directly from the street.

Another indication of potential problems then was the *language* of community mental health itself. For example, the new agencies were mandated to serve a certain "catchment" area, describing the boundaries of the neighborhood it was responsible for as the city was divided up into these areas. "Catchment," is a French word, sometimes translated as "garbage"—an unfortunate inference, at best, to describe clients, even in another language.

The Psychology of Creativity

Freud was the thinker whose innovative formulations and theories defined the psychological paradigm in the 20th and into the 21st century. His psychodynamic explanations were pervasive in mental health practice for a long time.[12] They are largely ignored today in favor of more behavioral and cognitive interventions and their vicissitudes, deemed to be more effective than talk therapy, which could not be scientifically "proven" to help. That behavioral therapies are more visible and countable and therefore more easily funded is indisputable. But as cultural paradigms change and new ones move to the forefront, old ones still persist; Thus Freud's ideas still remain alive in much of our thinking. One of these is his notion that creativity and madness exist together as interlocking twins.

Freud defined creativity as located next to madness in the human psyche—mistakenly, but forever—linking them together in the human imagination. Despite the discrediting of this linkage, it remains a pervasive assumption today. For example, to be an artist, one is thought to be a bit mad anyway and many believe that if the madness goes away, so does the creativity. This notion is often vitally alive in the populace and also among artists themselves who tend to see themselves as a bit crazy. Echoes are heard in their fear and avoidance of entering into any form of psychotherapy which might make their personal difficulties less, but, they believe, would destroy their creativity

---

12. And, I believe still are, despite Freud's ideas and personality theory being "on the outs" in contemporary mental health.

by eliminating altogether their need to make art. Artists tend to be particularly suspect of art therapy.[13] Explicit is the idea that the artist creates because of mental illness or imbalance.

Increased psychological clarity might cause creativity to cease, perhaps altogether, because the *need to create*—the *madness*—would no longer be there. This belief understands creativity as based in unresolved psychic conflicts and caused by prevailing mental dysfunction, even insanity. There are many romantic notions and what I call "floating assumptions" about creativity and artists. They have little basis in scientific or even metaphoric truth, but persist nonetheless in contemporary culture. That there must be mental illness for the existence of creativity is one.

Eighteen years ago, I retired from my job as a Professor at Loyola Marymount University, in charge of the art therapy program, and a year later moved out of Los Angeles where I was born and had lived most of my life to Whidbey Island, north of Seattle. In my quieter life on Whidbey, I stopped direct client work. Having been a visual artist since childhood, with professional-level training and experience, I began instead to make art—paintings and drawings. I found that my interest remained the same as when I was a practicing art psychotherapist: I was fascinated with the mysteries of the human personality and imagination and in particular, issues of anger and violence. But now, instead of working with therapy clients, I wanted to explore these same material issues through visual art (Chapter 5).

Unlike Freud, I do not believe that mental illness and violence necessarily go together and I do not believe that creativity emerges from mental illness, nor that creativity and insanity exist together. My particular interest was in making art to pierce the depths of mental illness in the human condition and I wanted to explore how, at times, it could result in mass murder. Of course, the loose restrictions against guns in civil society, often gave potential killers an easy and deadly method to express their more violent impulses. And the 24-hour news cycle made them famous. My exploration of the darkness in human personality continues in this book.

---

13. An example of this "fear" of psychology is that when I sought permission to use a representation of Georgia O'Keefe's work in a book I was writing, the O'Keefe estate turned me down stating she didn't want anybody ever using her work in psychology. This was 12 years after her death and in the era when every college student had a poster of her art in their dorm rooms or on their coffee mugs!

Chapter 3

WHAT WE KNOW *NOW* ABOUT MASS MURDERS AND MENTAL ILLNESS

A few, like Andrea Yates and Seung Hui Cho, the Virginia Tech killer (Figures 1, 2, 3), had long, well-documented histories of mental dysfunction which established a potential for violent acting and unfurled bright red danger signs. Nobody took notice or did anything. This lack of notice, acknowledgement of potential danger, or maybe denial (or all three) by mental health professionals, family members and the Virginia Polytechnic University community drew me to this subject in the first place. Andrea Yates had to drown her five children in the bathtub to "send them to heaven," and Cho had to kill 33 people at Virginia Tech, for us to pay attention. Retroactively and in hindsight we paid attention, when clear warning signs of violence were all over the place for both. Unanswered questions about *accountability* persist. When, how and who should act to ward off what has come to be the almost daily occurrence of deadly behavior? When is it the other guy? When is it me?

Narratives of the involved Good Samaritan who jumps in to help and the "Don't get involved" mentality co-exist simultaneously and paradoxically. This comingled dynamic also, exists within internalized cultural edicts and psyches of mental health workers and clinicians— including art therapists. We cannot help being impacted by the culture we live in. We can't help internalizing it, however acute our level of conscious self awareness. It is in the air we breathe. What we can do as an art therapist is try to recognize our biases and attempt not to act out of them.

What do we know now about mass murder now? *Not much.* Published research literature is at the very beginning of trying to figure out what has become all too common in day-to-day life (see Chapter 6, Chapter 10 and Addendum), what the Bakersfield, California sheriff called, "the new normal." The literature doesn't have much to tell us yet. What sparse research, there is, is usually retroactive, after-the-fact, and so far, useless for help in establishing actions that might be potentially predictive. Assumptions and myths dominate about what we think we know about mental illness as a motivation/cause for mass murder. Very little, if any is TRUTH.

Widely disproven, many people still believe the myth that the mentally ill are more likely to commit violent acts than the general public. Here there *is* good research: To be accurate, while there may be sometimes a correlation between mental illness and violence, *causation cannot be established.* Nonetheless, the idea that mental illness causes crime persists and is currently (even before guns,) the typical first go-to when investigators search afterward for motivations for a mass murder. People want to know why and law enforcement and journalists want to find out.

The impetus to establish cause fast for a heinous crime is an understandable attempt to make a chaotic world seem less chaotic and more stable. To know why a horrible act occurred helps to ease existential anxiety and enable a "them, not me" position—I am different than the killer and "normal. He is not!" This prevailing worldview claims that people normally and at best exist in a psychological balance and that there is a cause for everything. To find out a motive for a spectacular killing helps people feel that the world is orderly and logical instead of a chaotic, haphazard mess so anxiety and fear can subside. In the first hours after the 2017 Las Vegas killings, it was said that shooter Steven Paddock had "a severe undiagnosed mental illness." Initially, this "fact" was spread over news reports as the explanation for his crime. "Undiagnosed?" Tricky. Of course, "Undiagnosed" means that he must have had "it" whether he or anyone else knew it.

As it turned out, Paddock had never come near a mental health system, nor ever been diagnosed with anything.

Mental illness as causation persists in the face of little or no evidence because there is the widely held belief that mass murder is a crazy act, by definition, and therefore the mass murderer must be crazy. For decades, movies have portrayed characters with mental illness as sadistic, violent and with a strong connection between mental illness and serious violence. That this is probably merely the screenwriter's way of telling a tight, compelling story is ignored. Schug and Fradella (2015) cite the increase in this linkage over the years:

> Consider that in 1950, when asked what mental illness means to them, about 7% of respondents mentioned violent manifestations or symptoms, compared to 12% in 1996 (Markowitz, 2011, p.39, citing Pescosolido, Monahan, Link, Stueve & Kikuzawa, 1999.) That percentage has increased in the past 15 years in light of the intense media coverage devoted to acts . . . [of mass murder]. For example, a whopping 60% of respondents in a national survey conducted in 2006 reported that they believed people with schizophrenia were likely to be violent, and 32% thought the same about people with major depression (as reported in the Harvard Mental Health Letter, 2011). (Schug and Fratella, 2015, p. 3)

Can you imagine what the numbers are like today?

Fear of violence at the hands of those with mental dysfunction has profound consequences: it stigmatizes mental illness and *stigma* adds to the difficulties, both intrapsychically and socially, making it even more difficult for people who are mentally ill to live a functional life.

One thing we *do* know is that ready access to guns in this country and their prevalence can, in the flick of an eye, put deadly danger in the hands of angry people. That tighter gun laws were not voted in after the heinous Stony Brook massacre in which small children were killed, was shocking to many and indicative of the tremendous difficulties—perhaps impossibilities—-of improving the U.S. violence environment by tighter regulation of guns.

Who Does Them?

Generally, it is *adult white males*. The few women in my collection of mass murder artwork, both engaged in relatively *private* acts of killing, unlike the male mass shooters.[1] Andrea Yates, seriously mentally ill with post-partum depression and psychosis, drowned her five children in the bathtub to make sure they were sent to Heaven. She believed she was committing an act of motherly kindness and protection, Yates wanted to send her children to a better place. Ebony

---

1. As I write this, the news has come in that a 39-year-old woman shot three and herself at YouTube in San Bruno, CA.

Wilkerson,[2] age 32, with her three children, ages 3, 9 and 10 rolled up her car windows, locked the doors and drove her minivan into the surf at Myrtle Beach, Florida. Like Yates, Wilkerson was trying to take her children to a better place. Her children said to rescuers: "Mom tried to kill us. Mom is crazy." The February 1, 2018 wounding of four in a middle school in Los Angeles, by a 12-year-old girl, is thought to be unintentional although she was carrying a semi-automatic gun in her backpack. She said she didn't know the gun was loaded and her backpack fell and it went off. Where she got the gun is unknown at this time.

So far there is no research on gender and mass murders. But through observation, we can speculate that although a certain amount of force was obviously necessary at the beginning of Yates' and Wilkerson's acts, in a way, the water takes over and does the killing. Arguably, women engage in more passive acts than the typical premeditated act of collecting a gun or guns and going someplace to shoot and kill people, often for revenge—as men seem to do.

According to Louis Klarevas in his compelling book *Rampage Nation, Securing America from Mass Shootings* (2016,) despite the plethora of school shootings and the tragic killings by teenagers Adam Lanza and the Columbine killers, research shows that it is typically adult men who commit mass murders with guns. And they are usually white. According to Shugg and Fradella (2015) in *Mental Illness and Crime,* the addition of substance abuse can make a crime more likely. So far, that's pretty much what we know. Klarevas writes: "Mass shootings now pose the greatest creditable threat to public safety surpassing even terrorism" (2016, p. 17). The last decade has been the most deadly in the United States in what is widely seen as the most open society in the world.

Bullying, social media, video games, the more aggressive uncivil society today, media attention, male privilege and our culture of violence have all been accused at one time or another of causing mass murders. Sometimes, a combination of these is suggested. Our thirst for explanation is strong and that mental illness must have played some role is a given. Klarevas (2016) states: "All acts of violence involve a combination of ill intentions, vulnerable victims and harmful

---

2. Information about this event was culled from www.The Guardian.com>world>U.S. crime. Retrieved January 23, 2018.

capabilities" (p. 29.) He postulates a "trinity of violence: unstable per-petrators, vulnerable targets, lethal weapons" (p. 12.)

Guns, Violence and Mental Illness

In the gun shop in a nearby mall where I live on Whidbey Island, Washington, every time there is a mass shooting, business goes up because people buy guns to protect themselves and they buy them because they are concerned that the federal government is coming to take their guns away. Currently and quietly, a "concealed carry" bill is making its way through the United States Congress. If it passes, it would make a concealed gun carry permit legal in all 50 states. In other words, if one has received a legal permit in one state and the gun carrier crosses state lines, it would still be legal. This would mean that people could carry hidden concealed guns in all states. Even many police chiefs oppose this bill. Recently, a Texas gun activist sought to publish plans on the internet for a 3-D gun. Opposed through a legal injunction, he planned to do it anyway.

According to polls, a large percentage of the American public believes that restricting gun ownership would be a major deterrent to mass violence. But this attitude is generally mired in politics and ig-nored by Congress. If loopholes were corrected with stricter enforce-ment of existing laws, access to guns might not be the problem it is today. Restricting and regulating guns would not entirely solve the problem, but it would help. Nevertheless, the NRA (National Rifle Association) continues to lobby for and support unlimited access to military-style automatic and semi-automatic weapons on the basis of the Second Amendment of the U.S. Constitution which cites a citizen's right to bear arms.

When the NRA was first established, it took a far more moderate position on gun access; but now, it does not waver in its' support of a hard-right position and contributes massively financially to politics and politicians who support its beliefs. Shortly after the Marjory Stoneman Douglas school shooting at Parkland, Florida, American President Trump first took an anti-gun position and talked of fighting the NRA. A few days later (after the NRA met with him,) he reversed his position and advocated arming classroom teachers instead. He said he was praying and sending condolences. An angry Parkland stu-dent, 16-year-old Sarah Chadwick, tweeted:

I don't want your condolences . . . my friends and teachers were shot. Do something instead of sending prayers. Prayers won't fix this. But gun control will prevent it from happening again. (Traister 2018, p. xxxi)

Traister (2018) writes:

Chadwick's livid message was retweeted 144,000 times before it was made unavailable; the rage it expressed would help to set the furious tone for what would become the Parkland student's righteous crusade to alter the gun laws in the United States. (p. xxxi)

Based on the Second Amendment of the Constitution, that says the citizenry has the right to keep and bear arms, the gun debate is now so complicated and confusing that I think it has engendered a variety of apathy in many people. In the wake of the tragedy at Parkland, Florida,[3] gun control was discussed again. But there seemed a kind of hopelessness in the zeitgeist about anything important being done.[4] Most blame it on the Republicans, but actually this helplessness doesn't seem to be party driven. Even after the Republican baseball practice in which a member of Congress was shot, severely wounded and almost died, nothing much was done.[5] It should be noted that security measures for Congress are immense while there are few security measures for schools and what security measures there are for schools clearly are not sufficient. With Parkland, rather than mention the proliferation of guns or the issue of gun control, President Donald J. Trump called for an analysis of mental health as the motivation. Florida's gun laws are particularly lax as a "stand your ground" state with already a number of violent episodes this year. A former Republican congressman from Florida, in favor of the second Amendment said "Assault Rifles are for *killing* and should not be allowed."

---

3. Seventeen were killed and 15 wounded by Nikolas Cruz, a 19-year-old former student who used an Assault Rifle at the Marjory Stoneman Douglas High School in Parkland, Florida.
4. For some later hopeful news about millennials, see "March 24, March for Our Lives," Chapter 6 in this volume.
5. Because Steve Scalise was a leader in Congress, he had his own armed security detail with him at the baseball game. They killed the shooter. Without them many more might have been killed.

The Stigma of Mental Illness

Is mass murder a consequence of mental illness? If we could understand, acknowledge and better treat mental illness might that help this troubling, increasing public health problem? Would earlier recognition of red flags enable us to predict, even head off mass violence? Many think so. But mental illness continues to carry a huge stigma. It always has and does today. That it is often immediately connected to mass murder is indicative of the stigma. To have a psychiatric diagnosis, is at best a subjective endeavor but it means the person is *labeled* forever—sometimes from childhood on. Almost certainly then this becomes a self-fulfilling prophecy as the child becoming an adult *behaves* like a person with mental illness, while self-esteem is likely to plummet. Followed forever in school records and always preceding what she or he does, the labeled person feels abnormal and diseased and is often treated that way by teachers, parents and others.[6]

A person with mental illness is likely to have a lifetime struggle with the actual symptoms and disabilities of the disease. But in addition and almost certainly they will experience societal pressures, misconceptions and discrimination and they are likely to encounter a generalized extreme negativity. Remember Thomas Eagleton, U.S. Senator from Missouri who in 1972 was briefly the Vice Presidential candidate with George McGovern until it was discovered that he had suffered from depressive episodes all his life, had been psychiatrically hospitalized a number of times, and received electroconvulsive therapy twice? Recognizing the dangers of stigma for a public person, his history, had been kept secret enabling Eagleton to have a public life. When Eagleton's depression history became known, it humiliated the McGovern campaign and Eagleton was forced to withdraw from the Presidential race.

The history of mental illness includes the asylum system in which the sick person could be hospitalized, involuntarily, sometimes for life and put as far out of sight of the general public as possible. (Unsolvable problems are usually moved to invisibility.) For example, there are those who believe contemporary U.S. Senior Communities

---

6. Washington State has a law making it legal to pay less to people with disabilities in employment. Originally this law aimed to achieve employment for disabled people. In this era it seems especially discriminatory and unequal.

fulfill the promise of making the elderly invisible by removing them from integration in society[7] and separating them out from younger generations. Ageist, of course, it implies that elders no longer are useful to society.

Despite the usual good intentions many mental health "treatments" in psychiatric hospitals were horrific and painful. Involuntary hospitalized confinement was used as a form of social control and as a weapon. Not long ago, husbands could hospitalize an "unruly" wife for not acting "feminine" enough or for not "knowing her place." Those who were "different"—including the poor—were often institutionalized and hidden, to keep them invisible. Stanford professor Ben Barres says "difference is not a disorder."[8]

The word "stigma" comes from the Greek. It referred to a type of marking or tattoo that was burned into the skin of slaves and criminals. The mark identified them as damaged or morally polluted persons who should be avoided. Common social stigmas concern "culture, obesity, gender, race, illness and disease."[9] In 1895, French Socialist, Emile Durkheim was the first to explore stigma, but it is Erving Goffman, a 20th century American Sociologist who provided the most influential exploration.

Goffman's definition says that stigma is "socially discrediting in a particular way: it causes an individual to be mentally classified by others in an undesirable, rejected stereotype rather than in an accepted normal one."[10]

> Public stigma is the reaction that the general population has to people with mental illness. Self-stigma is the prejudice which people with mental illness turn against themselves. Both public and self-stigma may be understood in terms of three components: stereotypes, prejudice and discrimination. (p. 16)

---

7. Talking about the issue of "invisibility" of seniors with my doctor today, I heard of a worker in a senior facility who said "they become a lot like children." But that is another book!

8. Ben Barres who died recently was Professor of Neurobiology at Stanford University. He began life as a woman and transitioned to a man in 1997. He was the first openly transgender scientist in the National Academy of Science (2013.) As an M.I.T. student, still a woman, he solved a particularly difficult math problem and was told that his boyfriend must have done it. He wrote extensively about sexism toward women and others in math and the sciences.

9. https://en.wikipedia.org/wiki/Social_stigma. Retrieved 3/19/2018.

10. Ibid.

According to Corrigan and Watson (2002), stereotypes are

> social knowledge structures that are learned by most members of a social group (p. 16). . . . The social group collectively agrees on ideas about people and thus also develops expectations of people belonging to the stereotyped group . . . [prejudice] fundamentally a cognitive and affective response leads to discrimination, the behavioral reaction. (p. 16)

Stigma in mental illness is a dyadic and interpersonal dynamic. Perpetuated by the "outside world," as a phenomenon of social distancing, it affects people with mental illness and their families, resulting in a sense of increased isolation from others and a loneliness that can kill. Self-esteem suffers along with any hopefulness for the future. Rarely, but occasionally, instead of being diminished, the sufferer is energized and angry because of the prejudice they have experienced. But typically, there is a sense of helplessness and apathy in the face of an insurmountable reality.

According to Friedman (2014), the stigmatized person *internalizes* the stigma developing a strong self-stigma which can lead to a lack of self-efficacy and a passive "why try" attitude. Self-stigma is known to keep people from *seeking treatment* and it is well understood that "social isolation is connected with poor mental and physical health outcomes and even early mortality" (p. 54). Stigma has been found to be one of the top reasons why people with mental illness do not take medication. To believe one has a mental disease which needs medication, is to accept and integrate self-stigma.

Stereotypes and stigmatizing behavior are not limited to the populace. They often exist, consciously and unconsciously, in mental health workers who treat people with mental illness. Like everybody else, mental health workers have their own biases, stereotypes and prejudices. It becomes crucially necessary for them to develop self-awareness so not to automatically project their biased attitudes onto their suffering clients, making already bad things worse. This takes good training and education and heightened self awareness. That mental health workers—including art therapists—are human is a given. That they can act negatively as human beings do and are the unconscious carriers of prevalent cultural beliefs is also a given. That they can learn to do better is another given.

Systemic Ramifications of the 1960s
Community Mental Health Act

The John F. Kennedy's administration Community Mental Health Act of the 1960s intended to get warehoused people out of psychiatric hospitals and into their community where they would receive adequate outpatient services, be able to hold jobs and live more functional and fulfilling lives. That was the very good idea. Over the years, what actually happened was different. President Ronald Reagan and others virtually closed the mental hospitals leaving the people who really needed them unable to be served and often on the street and the legislature cut funding. The nation's homeless population grew and became the problem it is today. Many intended resources and outpatient services from the community mental health bill went unfunded, underfunded or didn't materialize at all. As the years went on, the few services there were, were nowhere near enough to really help. As funding shrunk and disappeared, community mental health centers could not effectively serve the multitudes of people needing help. Therapists became dangerously overburdened and by early 21st century, many clients who should have been receiving mental health treatment ended up homeless, on the streets and jailed.

A philosophy of psychiatric treatment, long based in psychodynamic personality theory, could not be proven to help and with pressure from health insurance systems, treatments turned almost entirely to short-term behavioral work. The mission had become to stabilize the client often with the newer forms of psychotropic medication and get them back on the street fast. A worthy mission, indeed, but realistically and functionally inadequate. The mental health system became almost solely focused, on medication and intellectual and behavioral work to fix things. Drastically limiting the scope—some would say being more realistic–behaviorism could be shown to be effective and therefore could merit funding of the agency. If not directly behavioral, other forms of treatment largely disappeared.

Individual Versus Community Rights

Historically, individual versus community rights is an ongoing theme and struggle in American life. With the Community Mental Health Centers Act of 1965, legal focus switched from community safety (often as a form of social control) to individual agency, choice and rights. It became very difficult, usually impossible, to hospitalize someone over the age of 18 without their consent. Catch 22 here is that people in the throes of a psychotic episode do not usually think they have a problem. Unless, they cross a societal law and somebody sees them, such the police, when they are 18-year-old adults they are able to refuse any form of treatment. Particularly in cities, we became overwhelmed with homeless people and with incarcerated people, many of whom have serious mental health problems, but are stigmatized and treated like lazy, drug-addicted, alcoholics and criminals. Some say the prison system has become the largest psychiatric hospital in America.

Nature Versus Nurture Causation

The theoretical question of the nature/nurture pendulum underpinning and defining the practice of mental health changed. Forty or fifty years ago, the causes of mental illness were thought to be primarily *environmental.* Mental troubles in an individual were caused by family difficulties, not genetics. When I first got into the psychotherapy business in the 1970s, the prevailing notion was that the cause for mental dysfunction, simple to serious, was largely environmental. Problems were caused by immediate family dynamics and relationships. Within the family, blame primarily fell on the mother and, as in the culture, "mother bashing" was an inherent, unconscious and unacknowledged practice of mental health workers both male and female. Typically, the father, usually distant anyway and away at work, was left off the psychiatric hook. A typical example was in Child Guidance clinics where I worked for a time, in which a psychiatrist saw the individual child for therapy. (The child was the important "patient.") The mother, viewed as next important to the child's well-being, was seen by a social worker; often dad was not seen at all. In these years, anthropologist Gregory Bateson formulated his concept of the "schizophrenogenic mother" who (he thought), through her mixed and double-bind messages "created" a schizophrenic child and adult. In other words, schizophrenia was caused by the mother. The "schizophrenogenic mother" was an influential idea for a long time about the cause of mental dysfunction.

These ideas about causation provided the underpinnings for psychotherapy practice and were prevalent in both cultural and mental health settings. This explanation, circularly, provided evidence for more widespread mother blaming and bashing. An example of this kind of thinking then was about adoptive twins. It was believed that the more individualized and separate twins became, the better. Dress them differently and put them in different school classrooms. Adoptive twin sets were typically separated and sometimes even adopted out to different families because it was believed the environment of a "good" family would override all else. Genetic issues and the lifelong meaning to twins of their early separation—each containing the exact DNA as the other—were not considered important. In fact, DNA and it's consequences was not even known.

Just as erroneously now in contemporary thought, in my opinion, the causation pendulum has swung to the other extreme. Mental illness is now considered a "disease" or a "chemical imbalance" of the brain, best treated, usually by medication. The idea is that an individual with mental disease, like having a physical malady, has little control over the origin or expansion of their disease, nor is it familial or environmental in the specific sense. This is a concept that allows any accountability, guilt-free, to be tossed out the window. Advances in brain imaging and the notions that we can see differences in murderers versus normal brains have caused the cultural embracing of a "scientific" understanding of brain *determinism* as the cause of mental difficulties. Pragmatically, however, our assumptions about the brain and its directives are still largely interpretive and metaphorical.

In popular thought, since environment or family are now free from responsibility, treatment beyond medicating is often not thought to be necessary. In the attempt to make mental difficulties equivalent to physical illness, the theory of the cause of mental illness nowadays is disease oriented. Environments don't "cause" problems, we say, and it can be speculated, therefore, that environmental changes don't necessarily help either. The "invention" of DNA as a driver and the redefinition of alcoholism as a largely genetic medical "disease" rather than a damaging habit have moved things in the mental health community to a different direction.[11]

The current attempt to formulate mental illness as like a medical disease that one "catches" is, in part a positive attempt to destigmatize

---

11. There is a particular irony here in that many critics of psychotherapy in the early part of the 21st century, deride it for being too "medical model."

it (and perhaps even let guilty mothers off the hook). This redefinition is based on presumed advances in knowledge, science and brain imaging techniques. But the functional result is that this form of causation tends to *remove accountability,* responsibility and agency: The person with symptoms (still a largely undefined and wholly interpretable definition) is thought to have a genetic disease—a physical, chemical imbalance that, in many cases, is inherited.

How does this pendulum swing affect stigma? Recent research on mental illness and stigma has shown that people told that mental disorders were *genetically based* were more likely

> to increase their distance from the mentally ill and also to assume that the ill were dangerous individuals, in contrast with those members of the general public who were told that the illnesses could be explained by social and environment factors. Furthermore, those informed of the genetic basis were also more likely to stigmatize the entire family of the ill.[12]

The causes of mental illness are undoubtedly a combination of both genetics and environment and not one or the other. All thinking art therapists hopefully know that to theorize and make treatment plans from either extreme of the nature/nurture pendulum is not likely to be a benefit to one's client.

Diagnosis as Subjective Interpretation: Development of the American Psychiatric Association's *Diagnostic and Statistical Manual*

The Diagnostic and Statistical Manual of the American Psychiatric Society was first published in 1952 and is now in it's fifth edition published in 2013.[13] It provides a common language (no small feat) and

---

12. https://en.wikipedia.org/wiki/Social_stigma. Retrieved 3/19/2018.
13. The first edition of the *DSM* contained about 106 diagnoses. The fourth edition expanded 300% to over 365. Many of the criticisms about Number 5 were about how it pathologized normal human behavior. Some of these definitions are now in common usage as descriptors, such as "OCD" (Obsessive Compulsive Disorder) and "Bipolar" (pretty bizarre.) Overall, the use of the *DSM* has medicalized mental illness and increased it's treatment with medications. With the acceptance of the *DSMs,* mental illness is a "disease" and a medical problem, the symptoms and treatments of which can be looked up. Some critics say the *DSM* has been an effort to sustain psychiatry as a profession and uphold medical identity. The American Psychiatric Association which publishes the *DSM,* with it's tight hold on copyrights makes over $5 million dollars per year on it.

standard criteria for diagnosis and mental health treatment and for insurance companies which have grown very powerful over the years. Although the *DSM* is considered the *language* of mental health and is taught in most psychotherapy educational programs, it is inherently unscientific and subjective:

> These shifting and changing diagnoses are more like what narrative therapists call socially constructed 'stories' than like real medical problems. What is considered normal and what is considered a mental disorder depends on the current attitudes of society not on scientific evidence. (Wedge 2011)

One great example, is that until the 1980s, homosexuality was pathologized as a sociopathic personality disorder and included in the *DSM* as a "mental disorder." Although a number of researchers found this not to be so, homosexuality as a mental disorder remained in the *DSM* until May 1974, 44 years ago, when it disappeared from the second edition, no longer categorized as a pathological disorder.

These days, the *DSM* is often taken as "Truth" (with a capital T) by generations of mental health workers. Nevertheless, each edition is merely a socially-constructed product of the Zeitgeist. As a guideline, it can be useful, but objective "Truth" it is not. It has become the "Bible" of diagnosing mental dysfunction which then leads to labeling which can follow a person their whole life.

The initial impetus for standardization came from the 1840 census in which there was a single category "idiocy/insanity."[14] Published by the American Psychiatric Association, the DSMs are based not on science or scientific research, but are the creation of committees of psychiatrists interpreting the existing data as best they can. Many see the *DSM* as a *political* document, shaped by cultural norms, the zeitgeist, pharmaceutical and insurance companies They note its subjectivity, unreliability and lack of consistency. Diagnoses can vary from one DSM to the next and indeed, from one mental health worker to the next. One psychiatrist might diagnose a child with ADHD (Attention Deficit Hyperactivity Disorder) while another diagnoses the same child with ODD (Oppositional Defiant Disorder[15]). Diagnosing for insur-

---

14. Then, in many towns, African Americans were all marked as "insane."
15. This week, I heard of a psychiatrist who diagnosed someone with Bipolar disease, rather than Schizophrenia because it was a "kinder" diagnosis! (Actually, it is.)

ance companies and diagnosing for "real" are two different skills. In my last years in Los Angeles, in the 1990s, I practiced art psychotherapy in an AIDS medical practice. The office billed the insurance company for the therapy session at the rate of $135. The diagnoses the insurance companies would accept then were "Depression" and "Anxiety." They only paid $25 at best, but the Catch 22 was if these diagnostic labels were on an insurance form, the client was psychiatrically labeled and would never be eligible for Disability payment in the future, because of the pre-existing condition clause.

The prevalent idea that if a mental health worker can make an accurate diagnosis according to the *DSM,* it will lead to an obvious treatment plan is fallacious at best. Human beings are wonderfully different and thankfully quite impossible to pigeon hole. Mental health practice remains an art, not a science. But the very act of diagnosing is a validation of labeling and indicates that the person has a medical disease. How often have we heard about an out-of-control child: "he has mental problems, so there is nothing to do about it"? The skilled therapist must recognize that she or he is working with *a unique human being* and all the complexities and mysteries thereof, and not a standardized one-size-fits-all diagnosis.

Diagnosing Children: Advantages and Disadvantages of Labeling

Early diagnosis of problems including diagnostic labeling of children (sometimes as young as two or three) who exhibit learning or intellectual disabilities, or emotional disturbances has been widespread in schools for many decades because it is believed that the earlier-the-better leads to better prevention. A child's acting out—minimal or maximal—may be genetic, developmental, indicative of underlying mental health issues, a result of home environment and parenting or combinations of all. It can even be normal behavior that has been misinterpreted by untrained or culturally biased and contextualized adults. Tides change: Sometimes, culturally defined difference, such as race or gender is a disease. "Different" is often a code word for "abnormal." To be labeled abnormal can have serious repercussions for a child or adult. Here is the conundrum.

On the one hand, the prevalent (and not erroneous) idea is that early diagnosis and treatment of a child are a positive preventive approach. Diagnosing as soon as possible gives the child the advantages of interventions, resources and services which can head off issues in later life. In schools, a diagnosis is necessary so a child is able to meet criteria to receive special services and so the school can receive payment for them. When the public school cannot meet the special needs of a particular child, the school system must pay for the child to receive educational services in a special needs school. All these resources depend on an evaluated, diagnosed child.

On the other hand, once diagnosed, the student enters a world of psychiatric labeling which will follow her or him in their cumulative chart and beyond through their school years and possibly throughout their life. There will be both seen and unforeseen consequences. Shannon (2007) writes that psychiatric labeling *is* the problem and quotes Abraham Maslow, the eminent developmental psychologist who said "when all you have is a hammer, everything starts to look like a nail" (p. xiv).

If a "misbehaving" student is evaluated and found *not* to have mental illness, he or she is thought to be lazy, inattentive and naughty and may be informally labeled as that. If he or she is evaluated and thought to have mental illness, the student is *stigmatized.* Either one is liable to lower a child's self esteem—often drastically.

While the *DSM* diagnostic system is believed by many—including teachers, parents and even students themselves—to be scientific truth and stable, in fact it is not. As previously stated, diagnoses of the *Diagnostic and Statistical Manual of the American Psychiatric Association* are based on subjective opinion rather than objective research and vary edition to edition. In later versions, critics complained that the *DSM* pathologizes what is considered normal childhood behavior. Adult standards may be used to evaluate a child's behavior and what actually may be typical in children is thought to be a mental disease, because it is not what adults would do. It has been said that Huckleberry Finn who played hooky from school, told lies, broke the law, was naughty and mischievous would be diagnosed as psychotic by today's standards (Wedge 2011).

I think, a very worrisome example, is the widespread diagnosis in schools today of (mostly) boys with ADHD and then a resulting prescription of medication. ADHD is Attention Deficit with Hyperactivity Disorder. In an era in schools where recess has been largely abolished and there are expectations and pressures of early learning, with the attendant necessity to sit still and focus, it is no surprise that this is a diagnosis typically given to boys. It is no fun for a teacher to have a wiggly student in the classroom exhibiting out of control behavior and making it difficult for her and for the other students. Here we arrive at the dilemma of defining what is "normal" and what is a disease. The boundaries of patience for "bad" behavior have shrunk. Recently, someone asked me how long a preschooler should be able to sit still on the story rug. I said "about three seconds." I was told that the standard requirement was 10 minutes.

ADHD is vastly overdiagnosed today with psychiatric diagnosing the main method to manage a difficult child. Labeled as a problem in school and stigmatized in life, we are creating generations who think they are sick. Overdiagnosing is a real public health menace that leads to a generation of drugged, passive people, who believe they are abnormal. They have been told there is something wrong with them and has been since childhood.

Rather than a normal child having a reaction to situational stress, an "abnormal behavior" label is a mental disease with all its ramifications. If the teacher or school refers a child and the parent dutifully takes him to the pediatrician or psychiatrist for evaluation, all too often, the reported "symptoms" equal mental disease and the next step is medication. (And we wonder why we have an opioid crisis!) Many powerful medications such as Ritalin. have been used for years with children. Most have never been tested for children.[16] We simply do not know what long-term effects might be and proceed on blind faith that all will be well. Medications tested for adults not children may carry unforeseen side effects which can be lasting. Diagnosed children carry the stigma of mental disease. Many never get past this labeling. Their life as a functioning adult may be severely restricted or altogether impossible because of it.

Any child wants to be accepted, liked and do well in school and so do his or her parents want that. Medications tend to sedate a child making them more acceptable to the school milieu and to the teacher. "Acceptable" is easier for everyone in the child's environment—even though side effects of the drugs may be quite difficult for the child's day-to-day life. Good intentions abound. But this is a dilemma that may have grave and life-long consequences for our children.

---

16. I remember a research study that proved that medication AND therapy together had the most favorable outcome for mental health issues. Nevertheless, medication *alone* has become the favored treatment.

Threat Assessment in Schools

Recently, I became aware of a "Student Threat Assessment and Management System," (Level 1 Protocol, 2017 Version) used in the public school system where I live. And I understand there are a number of protocols that can be used in schools nationwide. This procedure is intended to alleviate or head off the rash of school shootings. For a specific student in question, a trained staff member completes the long protocol, answering many questions about his or her potential violent behavior Then the form is put in an envelope marked "Confidential" and placed in the student's academic or cumulative file. A second copy is placed with an administrator or counselor and a notification of the presence of this "Confidential" material is noted in student information. The protocol says a *meeting* should be held including school personnel, parents, transportation staff and the Probation Officer, if there is one. The student "should not attend this meeting" (Salem Keizer School District 2017, p. 2). Of course, this exceptionally wide range of people in the meeting insures that there can be no confidentially for the student. If the student was a legal adult, 18 years or older, this procedure would probably be unconstitutional. Most likely this kind of assessment is a legal maneuver for a school system. In case anything happens, would it cover them legally and financially in some way? It was developed in a school district in Oregon, is 13 pages long and states:

> This system is designed for use with students who are engaged in circumstances for aggression directed at other people. It is not designed for use with students who are suicidal, acting out sexually or who are setting fires, unless they are doing so as an act of aggression intending severe or lethal injury to other. (Salem Keizer School District 2017, p. 1)

Here's the perplexing root problem: Are we in an era where violence and a fear culture have become so prevalent, that we are willing to eliminate the right to exert control over ones' own data, where any form of confidentiality doesn't exist, where a potential for violence can be interpreted by untrained school people, and where the underage student is a second-class, labeled and stigmatized person for life? This might be the best argument for home schooling I've heard so far.

Chapter 4

ART, VIOLENCE AND MENTAL ILLNESS

The Questionable Relationship of Creativity and Madness

Questions abound about the interrelationship of art, violence and mental illness. They are pervasive in American culture, yet I believe remain essentially unanswerable and mysterious. As the human condition is complex and mysterious, so is creativity. It was Sigmund Freud who theorized the metaphor that creativity was near mental illness, madness, in the human psyche and that the two are connected. Despite convincing bodies of scientific evidence showing that there is no truth to this idea, it took a firm grip on the human imagination where it remains today. The myth persists that creative people are likely to be mentally ill, that artists suffer much of the time, and that they are more drug or alcohol addicted than other people.

In reality, characteristics that might seem to apply to one artist can be contradicted in the next and there is a good deal of scientific evidence associating creativity with a positive mood and a happy life. It is also well known that one of severe mental illness' results is *reduced creativity.* Sawyer (2009) writes: . . . Modern culture tended to glorify aberrant behavior in artists . . . this myth has sustained the artist but the person [who] is genuinely mentally ill doesn't have that comfort (p. 1).

Explanations for current mass murders maintain that the perpetrator must have had a history of mental health problems—even though they were usually completely undiagnosed and external to any formal mental health system. Mental illness in the perpetrator goes along with the territory of mass murder and is the expression of the notion that if someone could do such a terrible thing, by definition, they must be crazy. Could creativity and visual art provide a safety valve for violence? A mere 30 years ago or so, it was widely believed that the depiction in art of violent imagery, *was* the *safe* external expression of an inward psyche in turmoil or chaos. The general public, mental health practitioners and many art therapists themselves believed that a creative expression of a visual image of aggression sublimated and converted violence, effectively warding off and preventing a person's acting out of his violent fantasies. Then, it was widely believed that if violence could be drawn or painted, the person was not going to actually enact his fantasies of violence. Now, visual art depicting violent acts is often thought to be *a predictor* of a violent future. Today, the drawing of a violent scene by a student in a zero tolerance environment is likely to get him kicked out of school immediately.[1] Both beliefs are baloney!

Despite plenty of contrary evidence, connections between art and violence persist in the public imagination and live on beneath the surface of consciousness. For example, in spite of a vast amount of research and long clinical experience showing that schizophrenics behaviorally are usually not violent at all, the popular mind still tends to connect violent imagery with violent behavior. The crazy artist or tormented poet or suffering musician are all prevalent, common and dramatic cultural myths.

It is said that the artist must be crazy or there would be no need to be an artist at all. If artists gets rid of their demons, they also get rid of their creativity and no longer will they need to make art. It is their crazy obsession itself that drives creativity. In a psychologically normal person, the impetus for creativity does not exist. The need to make art at all is caused by some form of mental illness. It is not only the public that believes this, many artists believe it too. Any art therapist who has attempted to do therapy with an artist knows this well. Many artists shy away from undergoing treatment for even severe psychological dysfunctions because they think it will also cure them of their creativity. Long ago, as an art psychotherapist, I led a brief art therapy group in an art school. It was extremely difficult to recruit people for the group and to engage them in this form of art making.

---

1. Some information for this section has been collected from Stone Lombardi, K. (April 27, 1997). "Exploring artistic creativity and its link to madness." "New York: *New York Times*," "Creativity and mental illness-Wikipedia. https://en.wikipedia.org/wiki/Creativity_and_mental_illness. Retrieved 4/30/2018/ andKeith Sawyer's "Myth of the Mentally Ill Creative," http://keithsawyer.wordpress .com/2009/08/the_myth_ of_the_mentally_ill_creative/ Blog entry.

This generalized abhorrence, even downright fear, of the application of psychology has been widely expressed by many artists, famously including painter Georgia O'Keefe who hated that her work might be interpreted psychologically. Seven years after her death, when I was writing a chapter on O'Keefe in a book I was working on and sought permission to reprint one of her paintings, I was told by her estate that they would not give permission. The reason given was that "Miss O'Keefe did not want her work to be connected to anything psychological." When I am engaged in my own art making, I "turn off" my art therapist/psychologist self and my art critic self, because I believe these forms of thinking inhibit and often stop altogether the creative process. That creativity is fragile and needs protection (especially perhaps from psychological interpretation) is a widespread idea that speaks to it as complicated, mysterious and inexplicably deep.

That there *is* a relationship between creativity and mental illness has an extensive anecdotal history and has been studied for decades. Aristotle said: "No excellent soul is exempt from a mixture of madness." The ancient Greeks believed that creativity came externally from the gods, specifically the Muses. Contradicting himself, Aristotle's also proposed that creative genius was *physiological* and innate in the human condition. But for him, creativity and mental illness were irrevocably linked and he believed that exceptional achievement came along with exceptional melancholy. Romantic writers felt similarly. Lord Byron wrote "we of the craft are all crazy. Some are affected by gaiety, others with melancholy, but all are more or less touched."

People with mental disease are thought to see the world differently in an original and unusual way; they are believed to see things that others cannot. So are artists. Some famous creatives believed to be afflicted with mental illness are musicians Mozart, Beethoven, Franz Liszt, Robert Schumann, Charlie Parker, Amy Winehouse and Brian Wilson of the Beach Boys, writers Lord Byron, Herman Melville, Dostoyevsky, Ernest Hemingway, Virginia Woolf, Robert Lowell, Sylvia Plath, and David Foster Wallace, visual artists Michaelangelo, Edward Munch, Claude Monet, Vincent Van Gogh, Charles Shultz, Andy Warhol and scientist Albert Einstein.

Kay Redfield Jamison, motivated by her own illness, researched manic-depressive illness (now usually called "bipolar") and creatives (Redfield Jamison 1994, 1995). She argues that biopolar disorder and affective disorders, such as depression and anxiety occur more in people in the creative professions such as actors, artists, comedians, authors, performers and poets. Creative people who may have been affected by bipolar disease include Beethoven, Virginia Woolf, Ernest Hemingway, Isaac Newton and Judy Garland. It is speculated that creatives have smaller amounts of latent inhibition—the person's unconscious ability to screen out unimportant stimuli. To have less latent inhibition can be connected to psychosis and some believe it contributes to original thinking as well.

While there are studies in which the data argue for the link between creativity and madness, the number of successful creatives *without* mental illness dwarfs those who might have it. There are plenty of creative people throughout history and in modern times—William Shakespeare, Bach and Jane Austin to name a few—without evidence of mental disorder. Indeed, it is well known that heightened episodes of mental illness actually inhibit creativity and may stop it altogether. The "pro" research has been termed legends based on subjective and anecdotal data.[2]

In this chapter, I briefly consider the relationship between creativity and mental illness in Adolph Hitler, serial killers, psychiatrically institutionalized artist Martin Ramiriz, Outsider artist Henry Darger and in my experience as an Expert Witness in the penalty phase of the trial of a serial killer who made art since he was a teenager.

Hitler as an Artist[3]

The terrible acts committed by Hitler and others in his name are well-known and are not considered here. Rather, it is a lesser known or understood aspect of Hitler that is the focus of this section: Adolph Hitler as an artist. The comment "If Hitler had only been accepted to art school, history might have been different" has become a cliche— spoken ironically and humorously, but the fact is today, more than 70

---

2. Despite the fact, that my section on a potential link between creativity and madness was intended to be only a few pages in this book and to serve as an introduction to the rest of the chapter, I noticed that there are many more paragraphs describing the positive possibility of a link than the one paragraph above that questions this link. One can only assume that the persistent image of the "crazy artist" is a more intriguing notion for popular culture and the human imagination than the possibility of any form of artistic and creative normalcy.

3. Some information for this section is from P. Schjeldahl, https://w.w.w.newyorker.com/magazine/2002/08/19/hitler-as-artist. Retrieved 4/22/2018, https://en.wikipedia.org/wiki/Degenerate _art. Retrieved 4/22/2018, https://w.w.w.quora.com/Why-was-Adolf-Hitler-rejected-from-the-Academy-of-Fine-Arts . . . Retrieved 4/22/2018, http://hitler.org/art. Retrieved 4/22/2018.

years after World War II, many people do not remember or even know that Hitler wanted to be an artist, worked hard at making art and in his famous autobiography, *Mein Kamp,* wrote that he wanted to be a professional artist after politics were done. His youthful aspirations were destroyed when he twice failed the entrance exams in 1907 and 1908 of the Academy of Fine Arts in Vienna. Even so, it is said that he told the British Ambassador in 1939: "I am an artist and not a politician . . . I want to end my life as an artist."[4] For better or worse, Hitler's immeasurable political and moral crimes were conveyed as a manifestation of an intense aesthetic sensibility.

As a 25-year-old soldier in World War I, Hitler carried his portfolio with him to the front and spent his spare time doing art. His paintings tended to be pastoral and religious themes, landscapes and architecture that had nothing to do with the dirty realism of war. When he moved to Vienna at age 18, he walked the same streets as Freud, Gustav Mahler and Egon Schiele. Poor and often homeless, sometimes sleeping under a bridge, he sold postcards of his drawings to tourists and made money as a house painter. Reporting on an American exhibit of Hitler's artwork in Williamstown, Massachusetts art critic Peter Schjeldahl (2002) in his "New Yorker" article "Hitler as artist" writes: "The young Hitler was wild for Wagnerian opera, stately architecture, and inventive graphic art and design" (p. 2).

Post World War I in Europe was a period of dramatic change in the visual arts. There were Surrealism, Symbolism and Post-Impressionism and Dada, Fauvism and Cubism. The majority of people in Germany and elsewhere did not like the new art and considered it morally indecent, elitist and incomprehensible. Of course, so did Hitler. Germany in the 20s, under the Weimar government, was a center of the avant-garde in the visual arts, music and film.

Expressionism developed in art and film, Schoenberg's atonal music was first written, while the jazz-influenced music of Paul Hindemuth and Kurt Weill thrived. Later, in the 1930s, according to Hitler and the Nazis, modern art was "degenerate" and was defined as acts of aesthetic violence by the Jews. During the Nazi era, modern art was banned from museums and galleries on the grounds that it was un-German, Jewish or Communist. Degenerate artists, often Jews, were dismissed from teaching positions in schools and universities, forbid-

---

4. https://wikipedia.org/wiki/Paintings_by_Adolph_ Hitler, p. 2. Retrieved 4/22/2018.

den to sell or exhibit their art and, sometimes, forbidden to produce it altogether. "Degenerate art" was the title of an exhibit, consisting of 650 modern works held in Munich in 1937. It's intention was to stir up and inflame public opinion against modernism.

As a teenager, Hitler produced art—watercolors embracing classical ideals of Greek and Roman art and decrying what he later described as "liberal individualism." Rather than explore the nuances of 20th century modernism, his aesthetic style and themes looked backward to 19th century style, neoclassicism and masters of the Italian Renaissance. His work was often architectural; he painted, in great detail many of the German buildings of the day. Judging from reproductions of his artwork, he was extremely skillful technically but unimaginative. He was rejected twice for entrance into the Academy of Fine Arts in Vienna. The judges said he had more talent for architecture than painting and suggested that he go to architecture school. The paintings he submitted were largely empty of the human figure and one judge noted that Hitler's works contained "too few heads." Hitler's rejection from the Academy may have come, in part, from his lack of social connections and his unfashionable "lower-class" style. Much later, he designed the stunning image of the Nazi flag.

Despite his appalling crimes, when he became a politician, Hitler maintained a profound artistic vision. His artistic skills in speaking, spectacle and design and his ability to move people through these methods, manifested an aesthetic sensibility. Without his inherent command of aesthetics, he might not have been so successful. He used his artistic talents to create a horrible torrent intended to remodel the world according to a certain taste. Even racism, in some sense, is an aesthetic vision in that it draws the boundary around something and attempts to make beauty by ridding it of its ugliness.

Martin Ramirez: Art of a Psychiatric Patient

In 1930, as a homeless indigent, Martin Ramirez was picked up by the police and kept in California psychiatric institutions for most of his adult life where he was diagnosed with catatonic schizophrenia. Before his transfer to De Witt Hospital in Auburn, near Sacramento, California, he was institutionalized at Stockton State Hospital where, about 1935, it was noted in his chart that he spent time drawing. He began to regularly draw at DeWitt, and is now considered to be one of the 20th century's self-taught masters. Ramirez died in 1960.

But that was when psychiatric institutions often served as ware-houses for the poor. Since the 1965 Community Mental Health Act and Ronald Reagan's closure of mental health institutions, the home-less, many of whom are mentally ill, flood the streets and have become a major issue of urban life.

Little is known about Ramirez, but we do know that he was born in 1895 in Tepititlan, Jalisco, Mexico[5] and migrated to the United States to find employment between 1900 and 1910. He spoke little, if any, English. First he worked on the railroads in California but with the economic depression he became unemployed and homeless. He was picked up on the street by the police in 1931 and committed to the Stockton State Hospital in California, known as the Insane Asylum of California. Espinosa (2015) writes:

> . . . eugenicists and racists...believed that immigrants were hereditar-ily pre-disposed to insanity and that massive immigration was the cause of overcrowded psychiatric institutions (p. 57). . . . Many APA [American Psychiatric Association] members felt that the immigrant population harbored a large number of "mental defectives" who would "taint future generations of Americans," if their entry into the country was not restricted (p. 57).

The first documented comment about Ramirez' drawing activity was at Stockton State Hospital in 1935. But before that, according to Espinosa (2015), entries in his medical file describe his drawing dur-ing his free time. An early file notes Ramirez as "talented" and states that he enjoyed giving his pictures to anyone who would take them. It is unknown whether Ramirez attended any arts-crafts workshops in the 1930s, part of the reforms of psychiatric hospitals at the time and focusing on making occupational products to sell rather than as any form of therapy. This viewpoint about art is one reason art products were destroyed in psychiatric hospitals. They were not valued then as art created by psychotic artists but were the product of a recreation-al/occupational effort and not considered therapeutic. By the time Ramirez began to draw, "Stockton had the best facilities for occupa-tional and creative activities in the California psychiatric system" (p. 99).

---

5. For those that want to know more about Martin Ramirez, Victor M. Espinosa's 2015 finely researched biography contains the first detailed history of his life and art.

During the Depression, "artistic intervention" became more common across the United States because of Roosevelt's Federal Arts Projects in which artists were sent by the federal government to teach in public institutions. During the Depression years of the 1940s, Mary Huntoon, pioneer art therapist established one of the first art-as-therapy programs at the Menninger Clinic in Topeka, Kansas. Menninger's involvement in art therapy and the training of art therapists continued through the decades (Junge 2010).

Ramirez's long psychiatric hospitalization provided him with a relatively safe and protected life, freeing him from worrying about food and shelter, which facilitated his development as an artist. No artist will ever have this opportunity again to be thus supported by a psychiatric hospital. Today's psychiatric institutions usually keep people for very short-term stays—a matter of hours or days with the goal of stabilization and getting the patient back into the community, hardly enough time for a even a talented patient to develop as an artist.

Before the professionalization of art therapy in the United States (thought to have begun with Margaret Naumberg), in the 20th century, in the context of the publication of Freud's theories, there began to be interest in the artwork of psychiatric patients for clinical diagnosis and treatment and the psychiatric community began to be interested in the psychology of art. Before that, in Europe, instutionalized patient-artists were noticed by psychiatrists. These patient-artists produced artwork spontaneously without any artistic enhancement or influence and, in some cases, despite severe mental illness. Hans Prinzhorn, a German art historian and psychiatrist, collected the art of institutionalized psychiatric patients and published his *Artistry of the Mentally Ill* (originally published in Germany in 1922 and translated and published in the United States in 1972). Prinzhorn appreciated the art of psychiatric patients for its artistry and aesthetic nature, but did not consider that it had any therapeutic potential as either diagnosis or treatment. He was fascinated by the art itself and it's somewhat bizarre nature.[6]

There was nothing then called "Outsider Art," which much later connected the art of outliers, including psychiatrically institutionalized artists like Ramirez, to formal art movements such as Surrealism and Expressionism. Hitler's designation of the expressionistic art of the

6. For a more expansive discussion of the context for the growth of art therapy as a profession, see my book *The Modern History of Art Therapy in the United States* (Junge, 2010).

day as "degenerate" provided boundaries for a whole segment of modern art which could grow to include psychotic institutionalized artists such as Ramirez. This brought to the forefront the interesting question, still argued today—can the art of the insane be considered ART? Here is a question which leads to all sorts of cultural and educational arenas, e.g. If one can make "art" without training, why go to art school or study art at all? It tramples on the overgrown thickets of the mysteries and potential definitions of "what is art?" In the United States, art and psychology and the psychology of art increasingly attracted the psychiatric community.

Ramirez's Biography as an Artist Within a Psychiatric Institution

At first, Ramirez drew with a pencil—the only thing allotted by the hospital staff. He used whatever bits of paper he could find, including memos. He glued them together with a variety of substances inherent to institutional life, including mashed potatoes, bread, water and saliva. In the hospital, patient artwork was not valued and was typically confiscated and burned. Ramirez hid his, thereby saving it Tarmo Pasto, a local professor of art, is considered to have discovered Martin Ramirez on one of his visits to DeWitt State Mental Hospital when Ramirez presented him with a roll of drawings that he had hidden inside his shirt. Pasto was a Professor of Art and Psychology at California State University at Sacramento and interested in the art of psychotic patients. By the time Pasto discovered him, Ramirez had been drawing for at least 15 years.

Here we encounter the stigmatization of mental illness: Is the work of mental patients, powerful and compelling though it may be, of interest because the imagery expresses the inner life of a psychotic person/artist or does it cross the line into a form of "real" art? And what is the difference? At that time, art created by institutionalized psychiatric patients commanded attention because of the former idea and was not considered "art" by the art world or others. As to Ramirez, rather than the "isolated," "marginalized" artist as he is often described in arts publications, in later years his art was widely appreciated and accepted within DeWitt's walls.[7] It is speculated that he was exposed to art classes there and to some peers using professional art

---

7. The well-known Northern California artist Wayne Thiebaud visited Ramirez and watched him draw.

materials who attended the hospital's arts and crafts workshops. Some of the medical stuff referred to him as the "quiet, retiring, little Mexican artist" (Espinosa 2015, p. 113). Espinosa writes: This paradoxical notion of artwork produced by a nonartist has been central in the construction of Ramirez's reputation, but it also has represented an obstacle to his recognition by the mainstream (p. 121).

Tarmo Pasto did not formally exhibit Ramirez's work as "fine art," except in a small exhibition in the Sacramento State cafeteria. Including a few of Ramirez's drawings, the exhibit was titled "The Art of the Mentally Ill" and was also part of the University's homecoming activities. Pasto used Ramirez's art in his abnormal psychology lectures at the University and to illustrate the interaction of art and psychology. Pasto gave Ramirez art materials, systematically collected his works and tried to create a protected zone around him that would facilitate his drawing activity. This last effort was furthered by a relaxation of hospital policies. Ramirez was an old and quiet patient who was considered incurable, which worked in his favor [as an artist] (Espinosa 2015, p. 115).

Pasto encouraged Ramirez and preserved close to 350 of his drawings, one of the largest bodies of work preserved by a psychiatric patient-artist. Later, Pasto lived on the DeWitt Hospital grounds with his wife and two children and in the 1960s conducted a research project funded by the National Institute of Mental Health to categorize the art of institutionalized psychiatric patients and prisoners in the state Department of Corrections.

There is an interesting crossover here into art therapy: Fascinated by the psychology of institutionalized and incarcerated patients, Pasto met Don Uhlin, also a Professor at Cal State Sacramento who was interested in the same thing. (Uhlin later owned, a few of Ramirez's drawings.) In 1973, Uhlin established an art therapy master's degree program at what was then called Sacramento State College. It was one of the first such programs on the west coast and one of the very few in a public university (Junge 2010). Unfortunately, it no longer exists.

We know that from his early years in the institution, Ramirez liked to draw. But we can speculate, that as he began to do artwork "out in the open," after having spent a long time in a mental institution, Ramirez's deep involvement in his drawing, might have been a meditative process, not only helping him to pass what may have seemed endless time, but also enabling an escape from the realities of his immediate environment and even the vagaries of his mind. This is what deep engagement in the creative process does. Ramirez's strange, obsessive drawings which in its iconography often manifested elements of his past life, must have taken him a long time to do. As an art therapist, I can imagine he worked many days on them, returning again and again, and that they provided a sense of continuity, pleasure and a surcease from institutional life. I speculate that Ramirez's artwork provided an ongoing and continuous loud silence that in some way signified continuing his life and identity.

Description of Ramirez's Work

Martin Ramirez's artwork is recognizable for it's obsessive, powerful linear quality, typically filling up all the space of the page. Even when his forms have negative space around them (which is not often) there is no sketchiness or indecisiveness about the strong lines. Outer edges of shapes are defined and complete with lines and patterns inside. His paper is often pieced together. Many are long, rather than rectangular which could be interpreted as roads. Ramirez's content is often reminiscent of his life in Mexico, reflecting folk traditions, horseback riders, many of whom seem to be fighters from the Mexican Revolution[8] with guns and ammunition draped around their body and Catholic icons such as Madonnas. There are also many images of trains entering and exiting tunnels and tunnels without trains at all.

Along with content, the art therapist notices *process:* Ramirez's artwork has a signature style. Nowhere is there empty space. Ramirez's created world, reflected in his art, is static and unchanging. Never is there a dynamic sense to the lines or shapes implying a potential to move. This is beyond mere primitive or self taught artistry. Rather, it is artistic intention. Ramirez's images are solid and stable, and characteristically fill the page top to bottom. Line accompanies line to the end of the paper. At times, minute repetitive patterns are used. If there is a recognizable image, for example of a man on horseback, it is portrayed within a contained space with boundaries on all sides.

---

8. According to Espinosa (2015,) Ramirez was 15 years old when the Mexican Revolution broke out in 1910.

The Meanings of Martin Ramirez's Artwork

Ramirez was an immigrant in a strange land, who had lost his Mexican past and later his past as a railroad worker. He had voluntarily crossed the border from Mexico into the United States. But when he had no work or home there to attach him to his new land, he was collected by the police and ended up within the walls of a psychiatric institution where he stayed until he died never speaking more than a bit of English. Probably he was always something foreign or strange—to himself and to those around him.

If art is not valued and saved, it disappears, no longer having been remembered as existing at all. An example of this are the objects left at the Vietnam War Memorial in Washington D.C. At first, they were thought to be trash by the Park Service. They collected and destroyed them. Eventually, the Park Service began to see the objects as valuable and perhaps even art. They began to save them, collected them and catalogued them. The hospital staff where Ramirez was institutionalized destroyed art products, but luckily, Ramirez valued his own artworks and hid them from the general destruction.

Concretely on paper, Ramirez's imagery remained. It existed in space and over time must have provided this immigrant an *identity*. He was the first person to value the drawings by saving them and eventually amassed a vast collection which he kept near him, even hiding them in his shirt at the time artwork was destroyed in the hospital. More directly, as his artwork came out into the open and Tarmo Pasto "discovered" him, Ramirez began to be noticed and appreciated by the hospital and it's staff, among others. With Pasto's recognition and support, Ramirez spent more of his time making art. He used the art as an interpersonal transitional object—giving his drawings to people who were interested. He began to be known as "that Mexican artist" I have written before[9] about a woman who after the loss of both parents and her home began to make art, which she kept under her bed wherever she was. Her artwork existed as her concrete signal to her that she still had a presence and a life.

What might be unconscious meanings in Ramirez's art? It could be speculated that the formal nature of Ramirez's work, in it's consistent filling-up of space might indicate a warding off of a sense of loss and

---

9. Junge, M. (2008). Feminine imagery and a young woman's search for identity. *Mourning, Memory and Life Itself.* Springfield, IL: Charles C Thomas.

loneliness. Rameriz's lines keep each other company. One grows next to another and another. They fill the space completely; no emptiness is allowed in which unexpected, dangerous things might happen. Many have called this line work by the clinical term "obsessive," but they are more than doodlings by a schizophrenic mentally ill and hospitalized patient. As master art works, they have a more profound and universal meaning.

One can only imagine what it was like for Ramirez to live alone in such a place, quietly, silently and not speaking English. Although after so many years, it must have gotten more familiar, Ramirez's mind and heart remained with his memories of his past, his homeland and in his imagination.

Serial Killers and Their Art

A serial killer is defined as: a person who murders three or more people usually in the service of abnormal psychological gratification, with the murders taking place over a month and with a significant amount of time between them.[10] The Federal Bureau of Investigation (FBI) characterizes serial killing as "a series of two or more [killings,] committed as separate events, usually, but not always, by one offender acting alone."[11]

While there is plenty of literature on serial killers generally, searching for their motives, elements of abnormal personality and behavioral indicators that might be potentially predictive, I could find no literature or research on the *art* of serial killers thus far. Despite this, the arts have been recognized as useful to the incarcerated. There *is* some literature about the arts in prisons, it's uses and benefits for prisoners. In particular, literature focuses on the expansive California arts project in prisons first instituted in 1977 by Governor Jerry Brown and the William James Association as an answer to severe prison overcrowding and continuing until the first years of the 21st century when it eventually fell prey to budget cuts and disappeared. After 10 years, prison arts programs were relaunched in 2013–14 by a partnership of the California Department of Corrections and Rehabilitation and the California Arts Council. By 2017 this program established arts programming in all 35 California state adult correction institutions. The

10. https://en.wikipedia.org/wiki/Serial_killer. Retrieved 6/18/20128.
11. Ibid. p. 1.

mission of the California Prison Arts Project is to reduce recidivism and help inmates achieve success upon release, to enhance rehabilitation and to "improve the safety and environment of state prisons."[12]

Serial killers and their art? No literature yet that I could find, but there *are* pages and pages on the internet of serial killer art for sale and apparently an expansive population of collectors willing to pay huge sums for art and other memorabilia used or owned by serial killers. Virtually anything once owned or created by mass murderers or serial killers is marketable. Viewing killers as celebrities and themselves as fans, collecting serial killer objects as important talismans seems a fascinating and disquieting artifact of today's society. It is so prevalent that it has a name: "Murderabilia." It is said that George Zimmerman's gun sold recently for $250,000. Zimmerman is the man who shot teenager Trevon Martin and was freed by the Florida court on the basis of the Stand Your Ground law.

Most serial killers, though not all, are white middle-aged men and it is said that many of the collectors are women. Feminist artist Maggie Dunlap theorizes an explanation. She believes that

> women are especially drawn to serial killers, mysterious deaths, gore, etc. because it's the only place that [women] are able to access violence, through this kind of remote channel where it's disconnected from our bodies. In fact, for women, who have all either experienced or feared being victims, targets, and prey, violence becomes deeply imprinted on the female psyche. Being a woman can be (and, unfortunately, usually is) a violent experience. (Frank 2015, p. 5)

The sale of Murderabilia is, of course, controversial. In May 2001, eBay refused to sell these items which some maintain forced the industry underground. In Massachusetts, there was a court case about Murderabilia focusing on prisoners' free speech rights. In 2010, Senators John Cornyn of Texas and Amy Klobuchar of Minnesota introduced a bill in the U.S. Congress to outlaw Murderabilia sales. It is called "Stop the Sale of Murderabilia to Protect the Dignity of Crime Victims Act."[13] In 2011, the federal government auctioned off, on-line, items belonging to Unabomber Ted Kaczynski with the proceeds going to victims of his crimes and other victims. Known as "Son of

---

12. http://arts.ca.gov/initiatives/aic.php. Retrieved 6/18/2018.
13. https://en.wikipedia.org/wiki/Murderabilia, p. 1.

Sam laws," these legal limits exist in many states. Their intention is to keep murderers from profiting from their work or publicity.

Other than for marketing purposes, why would serial killers make art? As far as is known, few, if any killers made any form of art until they were incarcerated. An exception is Charles Manson, who we know wrote and played music and hoped to receive a recording contract. In prison, he created abstract paintings until he died. John Wayne Gacy (the "killer clown"), Keith Hunter Jesperson (the "happy face killer"), John Edward Robinson (the internet "slave master, who killed at least eight women), Charles Ng (who with Leonard Lake was known as "The Operation Miranda killers"), Elwood Toole (thought to have killed 65 people and in 1981 murdered Adam Walsh), Henry Lee Lucas and Arthur Shawcross are among the serial murderers who created visual art in prison.

A cliché is that art making is well-known as a form of self expression. For incarcerated people, art making may provide an indication that a Self and an identity indeed still exist. David Gussak (personal communication 2018) an expert in forensic art therapy and prisoner and serial killer art, speculates that there is a correlation between creativity and destruction and believes that creating art in prison provides an outlet for the narcissistic exhibitionism no longer available for the murderer, through murder.

The acquisition and improvement of art technique may indicate progress for a prisoner. It is said that Charles Ng takes art correspondence courses in prison. But creativity is not of value simply because of technique. There is no denying that to engage in the art process passes time, which people in prison have a lot of. In addition, to engage deeply in art making can create a mind state, not unlike meditation, in which a person flees the boundaries of everyday life, and as if in a dream, can escape.

Serial killer art is fascinating to many because they believe it lays out, in visual form, the inner workings of a monstrous, demented psychopathic personality. Many believe that art made by serial killers provides a vivid portrait of evil and, indeed, a visual map of a deeply abnormal personality that engaged in the darkest of human depravity not once, but many times. Serial killer art makes visible the peculiarities of someone thought to be barely human at all. It is usually strangely lacking in the natural proclivities of human beings and goes far beyond the outer edges of what is known as "normalcy." The fascination Murderabilia holds for collectors and fans provides a chance for them to touch the existence of unusual and boundary-less evil, which may exist in all of us, but is usually not acted out. This obsessional nature of Murderabilia fans and collectors is like the compulsion of a terrible auto accident where the viewer cannot look away.

The visual impact of most serial killer art is a profoundly upsetting, general strangeness with direct violence often shown. An internet article by Jacob Shelton is titled "20 extremely creepy and disturbing artworks by serial killers."[14] There are no benign still lifes nor landscapes here. The artwork has a strangeness indicative of inner turmoil and depravity and cannot help but stir up tremendous disquiet in the viewer. A generalized belief is that if someone had seen this kind of artwork previously, they could have recognized it's destructive imagery, associated it to the artist and the murders committed might have been headed off or stopped altogether. Here, we arrive at a central question of this book: Is violent artwork *predictive* of violent behavior as many viewers and fans of serial art believe? Simply and unfortunately, the answer is NO.

There are plenty of people, including children, who make violent and disturbing artwork. These images, may certainly indicate personality turmoil and aggression, including inner pain and suffering. Clearly, these must be paid attention to, *but there is no convincing research to prove that such art work leads to any outward behavioral expression of aggression or violence.* In fact at times, the canvas or paper can be a *visual container* for upsetting and difficult feelings, providing relief for the artist that their unacceptable impulses and feelings are bounded safely. Art therapist Edith Kramer theorized that through the creative process, anti-social feelings could be sublimated into socially acceptable art. In our time, this idea is largely discredited and certainly cannot be trusted in our current gun-obsessed environment.

Over and over in my work as an art therapist, I have encouraged people to put their most difficult feelings on paper. To externalize internal chaos or trauma into an image and put it concretely on paper can provide a feeling of safety, alleviate stress and promote healing. It is as if the artwork becomes a magic symbol that is safely distanced from its creator. Externalization and the creation of boundaries increases a sense of detachment for the artist and can promote a strong sense of relief. Sometimes the paper images are put into other contain-

---

14. Shelton, Jacob, https://www.ranker.com/list/serial-killer-art/jacob-shelton. Retrieved 6/15/18.

ers or locked away from view—even put in a closet with the door shut. I worked once with a teenage girl who made a "secrets box," in which she put her very aggressive drawings that felt very powerful, dangerous and overwhelming to her. She didn't want anybody to see them, including me, and could not bear to see them herself. The box remained with me. She would occasionally "visit" her secrets. She could take the secrets box out of the closet in the art psychotherapy session at times when she wanted to look at them, but her secrets remained symbolically contained within the box in my closet and she no longer felt their overwhelming destructive power, nor her intense need to ruminate about them. They no longer controlled her. She controlled them: she could take the box out when she wanted to, but also decide to hide her secrets away and forget. Would this have worked with serial killers? Probably not. Nevertheless, in the popular imagination, horrifying art is typically thought of as a definite visual clue to a serial killer's psyche to be read as a visual predictor of future violence. It is not!

Being an Expert Witness in the
Trial of Mass Murderer Eric Leonard

To further my argument that no matter how creepy or violent artwork is, it is no predictor of violence, I want to recount here my experience as an Expert Witness in the trial of a man who killed six people: In 1994, I was contacted by an attorney in the Public Defenders Office of Sacramento, California who asked me if I would serve as an Expert Witness in the penalty phase trial of a 22-year-old man, Eric Leonard, they were representing who was alleged to have killed six people They had a collection of his art since the tenth grade. His tenth grade art teacher had testified in the first phase of the trial that he was "careful and creative" and had "keen observational skills" (Gussak 2013, p. 160). In the first phase of the trial, he was found guilty. (He had stood up in court and confessed.)

I did a good deal of soul searching about whether I was willing to participate in a death penalty case and about what validity my interpretations of his art might hold at all. I had been an art psychotherapist since 1973 and although I knew there was little to no research that convincingly showed the meanings of certain kinds of art, I had seen a lot of art in my 20-year clinical career. I decided to testify on the basis of my clinical judgment and opinions. How did they come to ask an art therapist? After the trial, I was told by an investigator on the

case that he had gone on vacation in Montana. He had visited a friend
there and talked about the case with him. The friend told him that he
needed an art therapist. He said "what's an art therapist?" He found
me. I was the Chair of the Art Therapy Department at Loyola Marymount University in Los Angeles then.

How I Approached the Art

I was sent copies of a body of art by the man on trial, Eric
Leonard, from 10th grade on including drawings from his time in jail.
I was also sent school records, psych exam reports and other information. Intentionally, I did not read anything before I looked at the
artwork and before I testified because I did not want to be unconsciously biased:

> [I] wanted to come clean, as it were, fresh to the artwork without hav-
> ing any outside information that might tend to bias me. I wanted to
> be able to see as freshly as I could to make my own preliminary judg-
> ments before I got outside information at all .(Junge quoted in
> Gussak (2013), p. 163)

I was not aware of the specific details of the case and did not read anything about it. I knew the 22-year-old Leonard was alleged to have
killed a number of people, and that he had been found guilty of the
crimes, but that's all I knew.

I observed Leonard's art intensely and over a period of time at my
home in Los Angeles. Using my clinical skills, I tried to feel deeply
into the art, and through empathy, experience the existential world of
the artist. I investigated the artwork trying to understand patterns of
meaning that persisted over time. I made notes of my impressions and
assessments. In Sacramento, the night before I was to testify, I went to
the jail, met with Mr. Leonard and asked him to do a drawing of his
initials with markers and to finish them any way he wanted. I wanted
to meet him, to observe both content and process of the artwork and
have the opportunity to have him speak about his artwork. I also wanted Leonard's artwork to go to the present day.

At the jail, Eric Leonard presented as a small, slight, dark-haired,
inward kind of person. He looked almost fearful. If one has an image
of a serial killer as large and with a scary presence, Eric Leonard was
anything but. He was cooperative and agreeable. He asked no ques-

tions when I gave the directive, and immediately began to draw. He completed the directive quickly and handed me the page. His drawn initials were tiny on the 8x11 paper and were floating in the top left hand corner. The next day I testified.

A painting of a sailboat that Leonard completed in the 10th grade was presented at trial and I was questioned about it. I said:

> . . . This revealed a world in which night and day are very close, but the red day is very hot. It's dangerous. There is no wind on this day. There's no way this sailboat, even though it's at full sail, could sail, and it almost feels like it could burn if the sailboat stays there. The overall impression for me was of contained depression . . . the sailboat could not move . . . was stuck. There was not enough water for it to go anywhere. There was no wind. It was stable, contained . . . could not get out of this world. (Junge quoted in Gussak 2013, p. 166)

Of his picture, Leonard himself had noticed the absence of water and reflected on "the scariness, the gloominess . . . almost like chaos and decay . . . [I] kept on thinking . . . about the darkness, the chaos." (Leonard quoted in Gussak 2013, p. 166). I stated that, from the artwork, it appeared that Eric Leonard suffered from severe and chronic depression and had for a long time.

What Happened?

At trial, Eric Leonard was found guilty of fatally shooting three people at a Sacramento, California Quik Stop convenience store on February 12, 1991 and one week later shooting three employees at a Round Table Pizza Parlor. Ballistics testing on a gun found at his father's house confirmed that the shooting had been done by the same gun. After the second shooting, Leonard was arrested at his father's home half a block from the Quik Stop. The killings did not seem to be tied to a robbery—the rifling through cash registers seemed almost an afterthought. A 1991 "Los Angeles Times" report stated "the father had known for a while that something was not really right."[15] Sacramento County Sheriff Glen Craig said: "[Leonard's] reaction was very docile, very staid, very stoic."[16]

---

15. *Los Angeles Times* article quoted in http://murderpedia.org/male.L/l/leonard-eric-royce.htm. Retrieved 6/21/2018.
16. Ibid.

Police investigators could find no motive and decided Leonard killed to satisfy a psychological need. They called him the "Sacramento Thrill Killer." During a preliminary hearing, Leonard stood up and said he was guilty. At trial, he claimed he was not guilty by reason of insanity. After psychological assessment, Leonard was ruled mentally competent to stand trial, despite the fact that he had a low IQ (less than 100), the result of severe and uncontrolled epileptic seizures since early childhood which affected his brain. His seizures were probably due to Meningitis and he exhibited bizarre behavior in prison, such as sticking a hand in scalding water and saying Jesus told him to do it. Leonard's defense lawyers argued that he had a personality disorder.

After my testimony at the trial, I read the various neurological and psychological assessments submitted to the court by psychiatrists and other evaluators. Eric Leonard was raised in a dysfunctional, abusive, alcoholic family in a small town in the Midwest with highly inadequate divorced parents. Since babyhood, he had been a quiet child who never cried much. He had been severely neglected. This timidness continued through his childhood and in school. He did not make a fuss, nor act out. He was so quiet he was never seen and slipped quietly through the cracks of the systems never receiving any resources that might have been available to him. In early adulthood, at one point he grew hugely fat, then lost weight very quickly, which must had been a jolt to his physiological hormonal system and which some of the experts said caused him to decompensate into psychosis.

In the penalty phase of the trial, Leonard was sentenced to death. It was reported to me that one of the jurors had said "Sure, he's mentally retarded, but so what?" In 2007, the Supreme Court of California upheld the death penalty sentence of Eric Leonard. The court said Leonard had been "properly ruled competent for trial and that the question of whether he is too mentally impaired to be executed should be addressed in future litigation."[17]

Comments

That Eric Leonard was seriously impaired for a long time and was what they call "an inadequate personality" is obvious. It could even

---

17. https://www.sfgate.com/bayarea/article/Death-sentence-uphold-for-Sacramento-Thrill-257. Retrieved 6/21/2018.

be said, pretty clearly, that mental illness was a driver in his crimes. It is much more difficult to establish any clear causation for his later troubles. He was developmentally delayed, caused perhaps by severe and uncontrolled epileptic seizures since childhood which affected his brain. In adulthood he exhibited symptoms of mental illness such as hearing voices and was diagnosed as probably schizophrenic and psychotic. His withdrawn nature and quietness since babyhood kept him from the awareness of adults who might have helped him, such as teachers and school personnel and also as he grew, away from intrusion into any systems that ironically might have tried to get him help. He was a shadowy, invisible figure, on the edges of society. He went to Sacramento Junior College for a short time. I can imagine him as a quiet person, sitting in a few classes hardly noticed, then disappearing, still unnoticed. What propelled him to shoot six people is really a mystery of the human psyche. But it can be speculated that without access to the gun in Eric Leonard's father's house, six dead people might be alive. Despite his obvious illnesses, Leonard was found legally competent to stand trial. In prison, I imagine he is getting more attention and help than he ever got in life. He remains on Death Row.

Was his imagery the reflection of a potentially violent serial killer? No, Eric Leonard's artwork was anything but. Over the eight year period of the body of his artwork I saw, Leonard's art revealed him as a quiet, withdrawn, severely depressed and ineffectual personality. Judging from the art, there were never outbursts of anger or anything else. I remember a tiger Leonard had drawn in jail, all curled up, with his feet under him, quiet and still, unable to walk, looking like a declawed kitten. Viewing Leonard's art for clues, no one could predict later violence. When compared to the disturbing imagery of the serial killers in the last section, Eric Leonard's art is the polar opposite. It supports my premise throughout this book, that one simply cannot predict.

Henry Darger: Outsider Artist

Jim Elledge, the biographer of Henry Darger writes:

I began work on *Henry Darger, Throwaway Boy* in 2002 because I was tired of reading in articles, blogs, websites, and books that Darger was a pedophile, a sadist, or a serial killer—or some combination of them—without any sort of evidence. Their authors somehow believed that, by pointing to the torture of children that appears prominently on his canvases, they were offering evidence.

. . . I wasn't willing to accept the commonly held belief that the figures represented Darger's desire, that by painting a child being eviscerated, strangled, or crucified he revealed that he wanted to harm children. (2013, p. 17)

I first became aware of Henry Darger's spectacular artwork in an exhibit at the Los Angeles County Museum of art and was blown away by the intensity, uniqueness and grandeur of his oeuvre. It was the real deal. When I researched Darger, I became aware of a literature about him that tended to interpret his work from a psychodynamic orientation which I found to be neither kind nor accurate. In search of conscious or unconscious motivation, one author theorized that his art was all about loss—of his newborn sister (who was adopted out at birth) and because of the death of his mother from puerperal fever when Henry was four.

While "interpretation" or a description of patterns of meaning is a common and often useful technique in psychotherapy, it is simply a made-up story or theory and while it can be persuasive and important, it should not be considered "truth." Once a graduate student asked me what a theory was? I said it was just a bunch of ideas made up—usually by men. I planned to write an article titled "The dangers of interpretation" with Darger as the example.

When Henry Darger's art is considered today, he is all-too-often viewed as a pedophile who should be in jail. This idea is based on the contemporary cultural idea and context that all art is autobiographical and portrays an actual lived life or desired life. Henry Darger's art and writing, therefore, must reveal his actual life: Looking at his art, he is clearly a pedophile! The fact that a powerful creative imagination exists and thrives and that it can be entirely separate from "real" life is no longer recognized by the general public. This is a tremendous problem for artists who use their imaginations to make art and a living.

The major theme of this book is that *you can't predict violence from art.* Previously, in this chapter I have discussed serial killers who create disturbing artwork. From their art, they look as if their behavior is violent or will be. But then there is also the serial killer (Eric Leonard) whose art is small, ineffectual and anything but violent looking. Henry Darger's work is lyrical, idyllic with tranquil landscapes full of flowers and fantastic creatures and it also shows stunning carnage with young children, particularly girls, being tortured and massacred. What is reflected is the constant mystery of art expression.

Henry Darger was born in Chicago in 1892. We know he began making art and writing about 1910 and lived a solitary life in Chicago rooming houses. The last one, where he lived for 43 years, was owned by Nathan and Kiyoko Lerner. Nathan was a professional artist and photographer. Darger worked in hospitals as a janitor, a dishwasher and in the bandage room.[18] Every day he climbed the stairs and disappeared inside his room. We now know he was making art and writing. He left his room in the Lerner's house at the age of 80 in 1972. He stopped all artwork and writing and entered a nursing home. His artwork was discovered when Lerner sent a neighbor into Darger's apartment to clean it out. When the neighbor visited Darger at the nursing home and asked him what he wanted done with his artwork, Darger said "throw it out . . . too late now." Henry Darger died at age 81 in 1973.

Darger had a difficult, abusive childhood. His mother died when he was four and his father placed him in a Catholic orphanage at age 8. In school, he was an acting-out, intelligent, but hard-to-handle child. His father taught him to read and he was advanced to the third grade when he began. But he was bullied in school. Henry abused smaller children and threw ashes in the eyes of a classmate. As his father was dying of the effects of lameness, ill health and alcoholism, a doctor convinced him to institutionalize Henry, now age 12, in the Illinois Asylum for Feeble-Minded Children in Lincoln, Illinois. It was said that "little Henry's heart is not in the right place" but apparently the diagnosis was actually "self abuse," code for masturbation. Henry had been masturbating since he was six and had even been caught in public. It was thought that a masturbator was evil, a criminal and a pervert of the worse kind. Masturbation was believed to be incurable and to lead to a slow decent into insanity which most considered hell on earth. Darger escaped three times from the institution making his way to Chicago. The last time he was successful. He lived with his godmother for a short time, who helped him get a job.

---

18. I met a medical doctor at one of these hospitals who had watched Darger going back and forth with his mop.

At 80, when Darger went to the retirement home, his landlord Nathan Lerner asked a neighbor to clean out his room. What they found there was a 15,000 page illustrated novel, 300 watercolor and collage paintings some as large as 10 feet long, a 5000 page hand-written autobiography and a 10-year meteorology diary (Stewart Fall, 2007). Luckily, this material was not thrown away as junk. Lerner, an artist and photographer himself, recognized that Darger's creations were art. Lerner and his wife Kiyoko Lerner took charge of Darger's estate, publicizing and exhibiting his work.

Unknown at his death, by the early 21st century Darger has become an important and internationally recognized artist thanks to the people who salvaged his art. Intuit: The Center for Intuitive and Outsider Art in Chicago dedicated "The Henry Darger Room Collection" in 2008, recreating Darger's actual room in Lerner's apartment. In 2001, the American Folk Art Museum in New York opened a "Henry Darger Study Center." Although definitions of Outsider Art as an art movement are quite fluid and controversial, Darger is one of it's most famous figures. His work now commands more than $750,000.

Darger's major work, *In the Realms of the Unreal, of the Glandeco-Angelinian War Storm Caused by the Child Slave Rebellion* is his 1500 page, 15 volume, typed and illustrated rendition of the adventures of the Vivian girls, seven princesses from the Christian nation of Abbieannia who fight a daring rebellion against child slavery. They battle with overlords and bullies and are often viciously tortured and slain in battle. One of the main controversies surrounding Darger's work, is that the Vivian girls and other characters in the book are mostly pre-pubescent females with tiny penises. How to explain this? In Jessica Yu's 2003 video, one of Darger's neighbors, Regina Walters, explains it this way: "I really don't think he knew the difference between boys and girls. Elledge (2013) in his biography of Henry Darger has this convincing explanation:

> It's obvious that the Vivian girls aren't *girls* at all but hermaphrodites.. For Henry they represent the psychic hermaphrodites that he, and many around him, associated with belles, fairies, pansies, queens and queers . . . a female soul encased in a male body...A number of queer men in the earliest days of the twentieth century identified themselves as psychic hermaphrodites. (p. 169)

During the nineteenth century, gay men began theorizing about themselves, analyzing why they were men who were sexually attracted to other men and not to women . . . [they] adopted the hermaphrodite—a physical emblem of the psychological combination of male and female—as a symbol for themselves in art and literature. This is not something that was typically known outside of the gay community. (p. 170)

Darger is thought to have led a lonely, single life, never relating to anybody, but that Darger was probably gay, is reflected in many ways including in his life-long relationship/friendship with William Schloeder. Elledge provides convincing evidence that the Vivian girls' battles and savage torture and cruelty was a way for Darger to work out his own tortured and abusive childhood and his years in the asylum. Many of the tyrants in the book were named for people in his past. Darger spent many years creating a fantasy world in art and writing where children were protected and loved and despite desperate and painful struggles, eventually win against the monsters of war. It can be speculated that it was his art that saved him and enabled Darger to live a functional and long life.

Functional? Yes, but "normal"? Definitions of normal are slippery slopes. Henry Darger is generally thought of as having a reclusive, low-functioning life in which he did not relate to anybody or anything. He seldom talked to anybody but himself and seemed to become "crazier" the older he got. One person said he looked "homeless." Yet he came home every day from his job as a custodian in a series of Chicago hospitals, climbed the stairs to his room where he was the ultimate ruler, and for decades escaped into his imagination in which he created a rich and extraordinary world on paper and canvas. His room filled up with "stuff." No one knew that the "stuff" was a fascinating and important work of art.

In the Realms of the Unreal, he called it, yet it seemed more real, compelling and adventurous than anything in what he himself called his "boring" outer life. He laid out his tortured, institutional childhood on paper, fought the battles he was never able to fight in the real world, and WON, proving that children such as he, do win in the end (at least in the imagination).

How can we reconcile Darger's compartmentalized, secret inner life with his apparently low-functioning outer one? We can't. We cannot even say which was "real." After his death when his art was exhibited, reviewers and art critics labeled Darger a serial killer because of the images of the little girls with penises and the torture. Well-known reviewer John MacGregor is said to have written "Darger possessed the mind of a serial killer," "[he is] posed on the edge of violent and irrational sadistic and murderous activity," and called his artwork "the ongoing fantasies of a serial killer" (Elledge 2013, p. 318). Art critics and scholars continue to argue about whether Darger's art reflected a genius or someone who was mentally ill or both.

At the age of 80, when Henry Darger grew too frail to climb the steps to his room. With the Lerners' help, he moved to St. Augustine's Home for the Aged, where he died a year later. Like Simon Rodia and his Watts Towers, Darger left his life's work in the room where he lived and went away. When Nathan Lerner recognized the "garbage" as art and asked Darger what he wanted done with it, Darger said "throw it all away." Lerner didn't. But for Darger, that chapter was finished. He is buried in Des Plaines, Illinois. His headstone reads "Artist" and "Protector of Children."

Chapter 5

AUTHOR'S MASS MURDERS ARTWORK

Figure 2. "Virginia Tech Massacre1."[1]

1. https://en.wikipedia.org/wiki/Virginia_Tech_Shooting. Retrieved 12/1/2018.

Figure 3. "Virginia Tech Massacre 2: With Lights of Police Cars Approaching."

April 16, 2007, Seung-Hui-Choi, a 23-year-old undergraduate English major using two semi-automatic pistols killed 27 students and five faculty and wounded 23. He committed suicide.

Choi was known as a loner who rarely talked with anyone. Born in South Korea, he came to America with his family in 1992 when he was 8 years old. In the 8th grade he was diagnosed with "Severe Depression" and "Selective Mutism" an anxiety disorder causing him to not talk or not to talk with certain people. During middle school and high school he received therapy and special education services. Because of federal privacy laws, none of this was reported to Virginia Tech which remained unaware of Choi's previous diagnoses and mental health problems.

As a sophomore at Virginia Tech, Choi was accused of stalking two female students. After an investigation, a Virginia Special Justice declared him mentally ill and ordered him to undergo outpatient therapy. He declined. Because he was not institutionalized, he was still allowed to legally purchase guns.

At the beginning of Choi's junior year, there were many instances of disturbing behavior on campus and in class. Well before the events of April 16, his angry, violent writings for class assignment raised concerns on the part of his professors and other students. One professor recommended that he seek counseling. He declined.

Figure 4. "Mass Murders Trilogy 1: Murderers."

Along with the wooden-like symbol of a gun, there are a number of mass shooters in this graphite drawing. They are: **Naveed Afzal Haq, Amy Bishop** and **Jared Loughner**.

On July 28, 2006, **Naveed Afzal Haq** an American of Pakistani descent burst into the offices of Jewish Federation in Seattle shouting "I'm a Muslin-American; I'm angry at Israel." Using two semi-automatic handguns, he fatally shot one woman and injured five. It was said he had been researching "something Jewish" on the internet. The shooting was classified as a hate crime and not a terrorist attack.

February 12, 2010, **Amy Bishop**, age 44, killed three and injured three colleagues in a Biological Sciences department meeting at the University of Alabama at Huntsville. She had a Ph.D. in genetics from Harvard. Previously, several University of Alabama colleagues expressed concern about her behavior calling it "strange" and "crazy." In 2009, students had complained that she was "ineffective in the classroom" and had an "odd, unsettling way." Many students signed a petition against her which was sent to administration. Shortly before the shooting, she had been denied tenure.

In 1986, Bishop killed her brother with a shotgun. The shooting was ruled an accident because of her mother's testimony.

In 1994, Bishop and her husband were questioned regarding a letter bomb involving a doctor at a facility where she had been employed.

In 2002, Bishop was charged with assault after hitting a woman in the head at a restaurant. There was no conviction.

She had many previous encounters with the police because of irrational behavior.

January 8, 2011, **Jared Loughner**, using a semi-automatic handgun killed six people, including a judge and a nine-year-old girl, and injured seven in a Tucson, Arizona parking lot. He had a longstanding dislike of Gabriel Giffords, Democratic congresswoman who was holding a constituents meeting. Giffords was Loughner's apparent target. He shot her in the head at close range. He often said that women should not have positions of power and espoused many conspiracy theories.

Loughner's personality and behavior changed dramatically when he was 18 and he began using an array of drugs including marijuana and cocaine.

Loughner attended Pima College for a time but was suspended because of bizarre and disruptive behavior in class. His teachers thought his behavior was a sign of mental illness. He was not allowed to return to Pima until he had a mental health clearance. He never returned.

After his arrest, he had two medical evaluations and was diagnosed as a Paranoid Schizophrenic.

Figure 5. "Mass Murder Trilogy 2: Portrait of the Artist Dreaming."

Figure 6. "Mass Murderers Trilogy 3: Victims"

Mass murder victims scream silently, reminiscent of Edvard Munch's "The Scream." In the right section of the drawing, a monster, after Goya's "Saturn devouring one of his sons," clutches a victim tightly about to eat him. Bottom left, in a drawing secured by duct tape, a stoic woman waits. Half her head is missing. The bird with her clings to an archway, also waiting.

Figure 7. "Shooting at the Aurora Theater."

July 12, 2012, inside a midnight screening of "The Dark Knight Rises" at a Century 16 movie theater in Aurora, Colorado, James Eagan Holmes shot and killed 12 people and injured 70.

Holmes bought a ticket, came inside the theater and sat in the first row. After a few minutes, he left the theater through a side door propping it open with a can. He re-entered carrying guns, wearing body armor and a gas mask. He set off tear gas grenades then shot into the audience with multiple firearms. Seventy-six shots were fired in the theater.

Witnesses said Holmes seemed to be wearing a costume. Others expected a prank at first or a p. r. stunt. He had dyed his hair red and called himself "The Joker."

Holmes was arrested soon after the shooting, sitting in his car. He told police he had booby-trapped his apartment with explosive devices. A Batman mask was found in his apartment.

He pleaded guilty and then innocent by reason of insanity. Psychiatric evaluations found Holmes mentally ill, but legally sane. He was diagnosed with "schizoaffective disorder" and found guilty.

Holmes' journals outlined his obsession to kill for ten years. Details for the planning of a shooting were also written. Holmes' sister said he became withdrawn as a young teenager after the family had moved from Salinas to San Diego. The family said they knew he was mentally ill and tried to get him help. He attended the University of Colorado and saw a psychiatrist there.

This shooting raised questions about the entertainment industry and comic strips expressing violence. Cinemark which owned the Cineplex agreed to pay funeral expenses and closed the mall and movie theaters. (They were later reopened.)

A suit was filed by a victim's widow against the University of Colorado citing *Tarasoff vs. Regents of the University of California.* It alleged that the school psychologist could have prevented the killings by having Holmes detained after he "fantasized about killing a lot of people." In this duty-to-warn case, it was said "The protective privilege [of therapist and client] ends where the public peril begins."

Figure 8. "Woman Intentionally Drives SUV Into Surf at Daytona Beach, Florida. Her three children say she is trying to murder them. She had been assessed by cops one hour before." (March 6, 2014)

Figure 9. "Shooting at Sandy Hook Elementary School."

December 14, 2012 in Newtown, Connecticut, 20-year-old Adam Lanza shot his way through a locked door of Sandy Hook Elementary School and killed 20 children between the ages of six and seven. He fatally shot six adult staff members as well and committed suicide himself.

It was discovered that he had fatally shot his mother at their Newtown home before he drove to the school. His mother was a gun aficionado and kept a number of guns in the house. Shortly before the elementary school shooting, she had taken Adam to a gun range.

Lanza had previously been diagnosed with "Aspergers," "Depression," and "Anxiety" but it was concluded that these had not contributed to the killings. A report said that it was his "severe and deteriorating, internalized mental health problems confounded with an atypical preoccupation with violence . . . [and] access to deadly weapons."

One year after the incident, there was no new gun regulation legislation.

In the drawing, the fatally wounded childrens' names appear along with their images contained in cubby-hole-like rectangles. Adam Lanza's head and shoulders are bottom center. (He appears a lot like Jared Loughner from a previous drawing.) His mother, hands on hips is behind him, protecting. Horses bolt upward from the morass. Their mouths are open and their teeth protrude. Eyes are wide. We do not know whether they rear back in fear or are ready to aggressively pounce on the children below. In the empty sky, on a hill, near where the two horse heads come together, there is an elementary school.

Figure 10. "Dylann Roof and the Killing at the Emanuel African-Methodist Episcopal Church."

June 17, 2015, 24-year-old Dylann Roof, a white supremacist
and neo-nazi, killed nine people during a prayer service at the
Emanuel African Methodist Episcopal Church, known as
"Mother Emanuel" in Charleston, South Carolina. The dead
included Senior Pastor and State Senator Clamenta C. Pickney.
One other was injured.

Roof shot the parishioners after sitting with them in a Bible
Study Group. He said his motive was to ignite a race war and
that he almost didn't go through with his plan to kill because
members of the church study group had been so nice to him.

Roof seemed to have developed his white supremacist views
after reading about the 2012 shooting of Travon Martin, (the
teenager shot by George Zimmerman in Florida) and black-on-
white crime. Roof claimed "blacks were taking over the world."

He was arrested the morning after the crime in a car, from a tip.
He pleaded guilty and was convicted. On January 10, 2017 in
a federal trial, he was sentenced to death. The killings were
treated as a hate crime.

Dylann Roof was born in Columbia, South Carolina and went
to seven schools in nine years. He stopped attending school in
2010 and spent his time playing video games, taking drugs and
getting drunk. He had two arrests and was accused of trespass-
ing in the months before the crime. He spoke to friends of his
plot to attack the College of Charleston. Roof purchased the
gun in a retail gun store in West Columbia using money given
to him on his birthday. The *Washington Post* said that he was able
to purchase the gun because of lapses in the FBI's background
check system.

After Roof's arrest, he underwent two psychiatric evaluations to
assess his competency to stand trial. He was evaluated with
"Autistic traits," "Social Anxiety Disorder," "a mixed Substance
Abuse Disorder," a history of depression and "Schizoid
Personality Disorder." The psych evaluations stated that all
Roof's decisions were driven by primary racial prejudice.

Figure 11. "Pulse Nightclub Shooting."

June 12, 2016, Omar Mateen, age 29, killed 49 and wounded 53 at Pulse, a gay nightclub in Orlando, Florida. There were 320 people inside the nightclub that night which was hosting a "Latin night." Most of Mateen's victims were Hispanic. After a three-hour standoff Mateen was shot and killed by police.

The killings appeared to be terrorist motivated. Mateen was Muslim and had sworn allegiance to a leader of the Islamist state of Iraq. As he killed, he said "stop bombing my country," by which he meant the American-led bombings in Iraq and Syria.

Whether Mateen's intention was to kill gay people is controversial. It was said he asked a security guard outside the club "where are all the women?" Later, in the trial of Mateen's wife, the shootings were shown to be terrorist and not gay targeted. On the other hand, it became known that during his time in the police academy, he went to gay bars and had male lovers who believed him to be gay. At one time, he has horrified that he might have been exposed to HIV. He had been seen visiting Pulse at least 12 times previous to the shooting.

Mateen was American born in New Hyde Park, New York. His parents were Afghan and he was raised Muslim. Since 2007, he had been a security guard at
G.A.S. Secure Solutions. He was cleared for an active statewide firearms license and held an active security officer license. Mateen has passed a psychological test and had no criminal record.

He had trained to be a prison guard but received an "administrative termination" after joking about bringing a gun to school. Mateen wanted to be a Florida state trooper but had failed and in 2015 gained admission to the police academy.

At a police academy cookout, he threatened to kill classmates after his hamburger touched pork. A co-worker security guard stated he had talked about killing people and had a lot of hatred for Blacks, Jews, Hispanics, Gays and Lesbians. Mateen was a long-term habitual steroid user.

Chapter 6

SOME MASS MURDERS IN THE UNITED STATES OCTOBER 2017–SEPTEMBER 2018

Introduction

During the writing of this book, I began to document the mass murders that happened almost daily. This chapter includes 16 of these descriptions over an 1-month period—more than one a month. (And I'm sure there were more.) None were terrorist motivated. Most shooters were adult white American men and many seemed to have premeditated plans.

October 1, 2017.
Las Vegas Strip Shooting from Mandalay Bay Resort[1]

With 58 killed and more than 500 wounded, this mass shooting was the deadliest in history. The assailant shot from the 32nd floor, Room 135 of the Mandalay Bay Resort, below into the Route 91 Harvest Festival, an annual Las Vegas music event across the street with 22,000 in attendance. Country music singer Jason Aldean had just begun his performance.

Shooting continued for 10–15 minutes before hotel security guards burst into the hotel room and found the shooter dead, along with 23 guns and a plan.

The killings were done by Stephen Paddock, age 64, using an assault rifle. It was clearly, a well-planned, premeditated attack, Paddock had taken 23 guns and thousands of rounds of ammunition into

---

1. Some of this information is from https://www.washingtonpost.com/graphics/2017/national /las-vegas-shooting/?utm_term- . . . Retrieved 10/1/18.

his hotel suite and is believed to have fired from two hotel windows to get different angles.

Soon after the Las Vegas shootings, the gunman Stephen Paddock, from Mesquite, Nevada was alleged to have a "severe, undiagnosed mental illness" although this was never proven. (The word "undiagnosed" lets everybody off the hook.) The Las Vegas shooter, whom the Las Vegas sheriff called "disturbed and dangerous" was known as a gambler, who liked women, had plenty of money and avoided contact with other people. He had virtually no earlier contact with the law or mental health. Finally, police called him a "lone wolf" killer.

November 5, 2017.
Mass Murder at a Baptist Church in Texas

A mass murder event occurred in a Baptist church in the small town of Sutherland Springs, Texas near San Antonio. Twenty-six people were killed and 20 wounded. The killing was done by a white man with an assault rifle who was having domestic arguments with his family. His (ex) mother-in law attended the church, although she was not there when the shooting occurred. Days after the shooting, it became known that some years earlier the gunman had escaped from an inpatient psychiatric hospital.

It was said that this Texas shooter had a long history of "mental health issues." He had been in a military prison for assaulting his wife and child, and afterward was given a dishonorable discharge. He had also been in a psychiatric institution from which he escaped. He applied for a permit to carry a gun and was turned down because of his mental health history. Somehow afterward, he bought one. That he was able to do so, was called a "mistake," and a "clerical error."

January 23, 2018.
Marshall County High School Shooting,[2]
Benton, Kentucky Plus Some Other Kentucky School Shootings

About 8 a.m., a 15 year old student opened fire with a handgun at Marshall County High School in Benton, Kentucky, a small town near Louisville. He killed two students, both 15 and injured 18. His motive

---

2. *Fox News.* Retrieved January 29, 2018.

is unknown. In the first 23 days of 2018, there have been at least 11 school shootings.

Kentucky has a long history of school shootings. On January 18, 1993 at East Carter High School in Grayson, Kentucky,[3] 17-year-old Gary Scott Pennington, with a .38 caliber revolver owned by his father, shot his English teacher and a custodian to death. He grew up in an environment of severe poverty and unemployment but managed to be a good student academically. It was speculated that his teacher giving him a "C" in his academic work may have provoked the shooting. Pennington denied this motive and said his intention was to kill two people to become eligible for the death penalty. He pled not guilty by reason of insanity but was convicted.

December 1, 1997,[4] a 14-year-old, Michael Carneal opened fire on a group of praying students in a Kentucky school, killing three and injuring five more. He carried four rifles, a revolver, two shotguns and a .38 caliber revolver into the school. Following the shooting Carneal was diagnosed as a paranoid schizophrenic with an schizotypal personality. It was said that he suffered from depression and anxiety and showed evidence of severe paranoia in the school setting.

In the weeks before the shooting, Carneal took a .38 caliber handgun from his parent's room and attempted to sell it to a friend at school. His friend did not notify the authorities. He also stole several firearms from his own and a neighbor's house. The afternoon of Thanksgiving Day, he broke into a neighbor's house and stole weapons and ammunition. It was said he was influenced by Stephen King's book *Rage* and learned to shoot accurately by playing video games.

February 1, 2018.
School Shooting, Los Angeles, California[5]

Inside a seventh-grade classroom at Sal Castro Middle School, near Belmont High School in the downtown area of Los Angeles, three students and one staff member were wounded. Authorities do not believe the shootings were intentional. A semi-automatic handgun was found

---

3. https://wikipedia.org/wiki/east_carter_High_School. Retrieved January 29, 2018.
4. https://wikipedia.org/wiki/heath_High_School_Shooting. Retrieved January 29, 2018.
5. www.latimes.com/local/lanow/la-me-inside-Belmont-High-School, and Yahoo.News. Retrieved February 6, 2018.

and the shooting was attributed to a 12-year-old girl who was booked on charges of "negligent discharge of a firearm on school grounds." The deputy Chief of Police stated that it was too early to determine any motive. The girl said: "I had the gun in my backpack. I didn't know it was loaded. My backpack fell and the gun went off. Where she got the gun is unknown at this time, but City Attorney Mike Fuerer said "L.A. has a gun law about the safe storage of weapons. Every responsible gun owner needs to take heed." Los Angeles schools, including this one, conduct random searches with metal wands. However, these searches are not only random but inconsistent and some schools don't even have a metal wand.

February 14, 2018.
Valentine's Day School Shooting at Marjory Stoneman Douglas High School, Parkland, Broward County, Florida

Using an AR-15 assault rifle, Nikolas Cruz, a 19-year-old former student who had been expelled, killed 17 people and wounded 15 at Marjory Stoneman Douglas High School in Parkland, Florida. The dead included teachers and a coach who threw himself in front of students to save them. While Cruz's motivations are unclear at this time, a beginning assessment of his background provides plenty of aberrant behavior and evidence of a dysfunctional personality, over many years. He had been expelled from three schools and was known to have a fascination with guns; he owned many and, as some students said, brought them to school a number of times.

He was an adopted child whose adoptive father had died ten years before; his adoptive mother died suddenly last November of pneumonia. It was a chaotic upbringing. After his mother's death, Cruz went to live in a trailer with the mother of a school friend. He brought with him many guns including an assault rifle. Fights over the guns caused him to be asked to leave. Another school friend invited him to live with his family. His new father insisted he buy a locked case for the guns before he could move in. The father thought he had the only key to the locked case. It turned out he didn't. Cruz's last family reported that he was respectful and followed the rules. Given his tumultuous childhood and the recent death of his mother, his "normal" behavior was not considered deeply abnormal, as it should have been.

There is a strong suggestion, thus far unfounded, that Cruz was a white supremacist. His last expulsion from school was for "erratic behavior" and because he had a knife. He was ordered to never come to school again with a backpack.

A few months ago, President Trump rolled back an Obama era regulation making it impossible for people with mental illness to purchase guns. Cruz legally purchased six guns in the last year, including the assault rifle. There had been plenty of previous erratic behavior and red flags: The police had been called to the residence more than 30 times. Neighbors and classmates all knew Cruz had big problems. It was said that Cruz had been in mental health treatment for a year and on stabilizing medications, but had not taken his medication, nor seen a therapist in the 14 months before the shooting. Even if the red flags are quite evident, as in this case, once a person is "an adult" at age 18, it is difficult for the mental health system to intervene against the person's will. However, anyone looking could have seen that Cruz was an obvious homicidal threat.

In 2017, before the school shooting, a YouTube user, after seeing direct homicidal messages on social media and Cruz's name on a post with the message "I'm going to be a professional school shooter" contacted the FBI. This information should have been forwarded to FBI in Miami, but it wasn't. The FBI acknowledged mishandling the information including a January 5th tip stating that Cruz had guns and the potential to carry out a school shooting. Although Cruz's name was on the email, the F.B.I. stated they were unable to identify the sender.

An armed and trained security officer at the school did not enter. As of this writing, it looks like there may have been three more security officers who were at the school and were ineffective. The resignation of the Broward County Sheriff has been called for.

On the morning of February 14th, Cruz refused to go to the alternative school he was attending saying "I don't go to school on Valentine's Day." The rampage seems to have been carefully planned and premeditated. Cruz set off a fire alarm in the school to draw the students out of their classrooms.

Cruz was arrested walking down a road near the school after the shooting. It was said, he looked like "any teenager." President Trump talked of mental health as the problem and made no mention of gun control. Later he advocated arming classroom teachers.

This shooting had the greatest loss of life from school gun violence since the killing of 27 at Sandy Hook Elementary School, of which 20 were children ages six and seven in New Town, Connecticut. In 2018, so far, there have been 30 mass shootings. (See Chapter 7 "Why Have We Forgotten that children suffer? A Reaction to the Marjory Stoneman Douglas School Shooting.")

It should be noted that Marjory Stoneman Douglas was a school that utilized regular and detailed drills against school shooters. Theoretically, they were well prepared. We can wonder how many would have been killed if they hadn't been?

March 10, 2018.
Three Mental Health Workers Held Hostage and Killed by an Expelled Ex-patient at a Northern California Home Treating Vets with Post-Traumatic Stress Disorder

In Yountville, north of San Francisco and near Santa Rosa in Northern California, a former patient of the Veteran's Home, Albert Wong, entered a staff farewell party with a high-powered rifle. He took three staff members hostage, including the Executive Director of the home Christine Loeber, 48. At the end of the day-long siege, Wong and the three staff members were found dead.

The Pathway Home program, which Wong had attended, was independent within the Veterans Home which is the largest in the United States with over 1000 residents and 600 acres of land. The non-profit program aimed to help veterans of the Iraq and Afghanistan wars cope with the stresses of war and the often resultant Post-Traumatic Stress Disorder. Its mission was to help vets re-enter society as functioning and productive members. Along with Wong, the three victims of the shooting were Loeber who was the Executive Director of the home, Jennifer Golick a 42-year-old staff psychologist, and Jennifer Gonzales. Golick is thought to be the person who previously had expelled Wong from the Pathway Home program. According to State Senator Bill Dodd "He [Wong] needed more treatment and the way to get more treatment was a referral. . . . Obviously, [he] didn't like it."[6] Gonzales was a 29-year-old psychologist and therapist with

---

6. http:abc7news.com/yountville-shooter-reportedly-struggled-with-ptsd-program/3200378/ Retrieved 3/10/2018.

the San Francisco Department of Veterans Affairs. She had been married for a year and was seven months pregnant.

According to Cissy Sherr[7] who had been Wong's legal guardian since childhood, when his father died and his mother began to have medical problems, he was never the same after he came home from Afghanistan. He had trouble sleeping and was hypervigilant about his surroundings. He worried about people who owed him money and hadn't paid and those that didn't carry their weight. Sherr stated, Wong had serious difficulties adjusting to regular life.

When he found the Pathway Home program, he said he felt he had found a path to recovery for himself. But he had told his brother that he was angry at the veterans' program staff after he had been dismissed from the program two weeks previously. Another brother, who had not seen him in a long time heard that he had stopped taking his meds and began to drink a lot.

Sherr and her husband raised Wong for a few of his adolescent years. They put him in Catholic school and signed him up for sports. But as a teenager, he also went to foster care and was raised by a foster father in a home with other teenage boys. He attended high school in San Francisco. His outbursts and fights sometimes led to his needing to live elsewhere. For example, he pushed another brother down the stairs, breaking his leg. Wong loved bringing his ailing mother special foods and spending time with her. She died last year.

Since childhood, Wong had dreamed of joining the Army. He served in the Army Reserve from 1998 until 2002, enlisted for active duty and was deployed to Afghanistan in April 2011, according to military records. He was awarded the Expert Marksmanship Badge which meant that he was given the most difficult assignments where he undoubtedly saw horrible things. After he was honorably discharged in April 2013, he planned to enroll in school to study computer programming and business.

Witness Sandra Woodford, a long-time volunteer with veterans and a veteran herself said: "I've seen PTSD patients go off. It's not unusual. It's not rare. It's infrequent, thank goodness."[8]

---

7. Albert Wong's history is taken from the *Chicago Tribune* article of 3/15/2018 "Man who killed 3 at California veterans home had sought healing there," (http://chicagotribune.com/news/nation world/ct-albert-wong-veterans-home shooting . . . Retrieved 3/15/2018.
8. See ABC News reference.

March 20, 2018.
First Day of Spring. School Shootout at
Great Mills High School in Southern Maryland[9]

A 17-year-old student, Austin Wyatt Rollins, with a Glock semi-automatic handgun legally owned by his father, opened fire at a high school 70 miles southwest of Washington D.C. critically wounding two students, ages 14 and 16. Rollins was mortally wounded by the school resource officer. He later died at the hospital. It is said that this was not a random shooting and there was a prior relationship between Rollins and the female student he shot. She died a week after she was shot.

In February 2018, police had investigated rumors that someone was threatening to shoot people at the school. Although the threats were unsubstantiated, security was increased at the school. It is not known at this time whether this episode was connected with Tuesday's violence.

March 24, 2018.
"March for Our Lives" Gun Control March in Washington, D.C.
A Reaction by Students to the Shooting at Marjory
Stoneman Douglas High School, Parkland, Florida

Less than a week after 17 students were killed on February 14 by Nikolaus Cruz at Marjory Stoneman Douglas High School in Parkland, Florida, student survivors announced a march to Washington D.C. on March 24th, 2018 to demand an end to gun violence. The group's mission statement reads:

> Not one more. We cannot allow one more child to be shot at school. We cannot allow one more teacher to make a choice to jump in front of a firing assault rifle to save the lives of students. . . . We cannot allow one more family to wait for a call that never comes. Our schools are unsafe. Our children and teachers are dying. We must make it a top priority to save these lives.[10]

---

9. Information from Hedgneth & Jouvenal (2018). "Student gunman dies after Maryland school shooting; two other students injured." *Washington Post,* 3/20/2018.
10. https://mashable.com2018/02/parkland-school-shooting-march-for-our-lives/ Retrieved 4/2/2018.

Cameron Kasky, a 17-year-old survivor wrote that enough is enough:

> If the politicians won't do anything about gun violence, then we and those like us will vote them out . . . I'm just a high school student and I do not pretend to have all the answers. However, even in my position I can see that there is a desperate need for change—-change that starts by folks showing up to the polls and voting all those individuals who are in the back pockets of gun lobbyists out of office.[11]

The march on Washington as a protest against gun violence became a national student movement and obsession and on March 24th, 500,000 were expected. There were marches across the country and students walked out of schools nationwide. They proclaimed their frustration with adults who have done nothing, they said, and with tears streaming down their faces, they vowed to power a new generation of political activism. Delaney Tarr, a student at Marjory Stoneman Douglas High School said "We will take action every day in every way until they simply cannot ignore us anymore."[12]

Organizers noted that rallies took place in 390 of the United States' 435 congressional districts. Americans living abroad joined the movement and protested at many American embassies. Neither Republican nor Democrat, the protest movement became a huge and visible incentive to vote as soon as they can for Millennials, who traditionally vote in very small numbers. Voter Registration became a common action of the protest rallies.

Thus far there has been little immediate action in Congress. President Trump, first promised the Parkland students he would help and would take on the NRA (National Rifle Association). But after a meeting with the NRA, Trump signed a spending bill that took no significant steps on gun control and called for arming school personnel and teachers. The Florida State Legislature passed an expansive gun control measure including raising the age to purchase a firearm from 18 to 21 and instituting a three-day waiting period on gun purchases. The Bill was signed soon after the school shooting by Governor Rick Scott.

---

11. Ibid.
12. March 25, 2018: "With passion and fury, students march on guns." *The New York Times,* p. A1.

Gun rights organizations and the powerful NRA gun rights lobby that has donated money to the campaigns of many politicians vigorously tried to squash any movement toward gun control legislation. They view the student movement as an attempt to take away their Second Amendment rights to bear arms. One pro-gun person said "I believe it is their goal to unarm America . . ."[13]

After the marches, will gun control resistance disappear? How much persistence will there be and what will be real change? Will it go away? Rosie Banks, age 17 from Sterling, VA, said: "They're looking for us to get bored. . . . We're not going to get bored."[14]

April 3, 2018.
Woman Shoots Three at YouTube in San Bruno, California[15]

Thirty-nine-year-old Nosim Aghdam shot three people in a courtyard at YouTube in Northern California and then killed herself. She is thought to have had a long-running dispute with YouTube, believing they discriminated against her content on her YouTube channel which she used to promote her healthy living approach and advocate against animal abuse. The three victims are in hospital in critical condition.

April 22, 2018.
Mass Shooting at Waffle Shop, Nashville, Tennessee

Travis Reinking, age 29, shot and killed four people and severely injured four others with an AK-15 rifle at a waffle shop in Nashville, Sunday. He was from Morton, Illinois and was wearing a green jacket and nothing else. A patron, James Shaw Jr., wrestled the gun away from Reinking or it was thought that he would have killed many more.

Reinking was known to police authorities and to the Secret Service for many previous incidents. He had stalked the singer Taylor Swift and asserted to police a few weeks before the Nashville incident, that at least 30 people were hacking into his computer and phone. April 22, 2018, he jumped over a barrier at the White House. When he was

---

13. Ibid.

14. April 2, 2018, "Gun control and fall elections: Moment or movement?" *The New York Times,* p. A1.

15. From https://www.marketwatch.com/story/youtube-shooting-woman-angry-at-filtered-videos-iden . . . Retrieved 4/20/2018.

apprehended he said he was trying to make an appointment with the President.

Reinking had a history of suicidal behavior in public places. After one of these attempts he was taken to a mental hospital for evaluation. It is not known what the evaluation showed, but he was released. The week before the waffle house shooting, he was accused of stealing a B.M.W. from an auto dealership.

Reinking had a firearms license and a number of firearms, including the AK-15. These were taken away from him, but were later given back to his father. His father returned them to him. Reinking was a construction worker. He had been fired three weeks before the latest incident, but was hired by a new company.

Reinking evaded authorities for 34 hours but because of a tip was arrested in a wooded area within sight of the apartment in which he lived. Before he was found Monday some Nashville public schools were on "lockdown."

May 18, 2018.
Mass Shooting at Santa Fe High School Near Houston, Texas

On Friday May 18th, 2018 at 7:40 a.m., Dimitros Pagourzis, a 17-year-old student began firing a revolver into an art class. He also used a shotgun. It is said that he wanted to kill certain students and spare students he liked "so he could have his story told."[16] Beyond this, his motive is unknown. Pagourzis fatally shot 10 people—8 students and two substitute teachers. Fourteen others were wounded including Pagourzis who had intended to commit suicide.

Pagourzis was engaged by police officers at the school four minutes after he began shooting. One officer was severely wounded. After shooting into the ceramics room which was between the two art rooms, Pagourzis was again engaged by a Texas State Trooper and a Santa Fe school police officer who attempted to have him surrender peacefully. Reportedly, Pagourzis fired his weapons and threatened to shoot the officers. After he was injured, he surrendered. The whole thing took about 15 minutes. A number of explosive devices including a Molotov cocktail were found at the school and off campus.

The guns were legally owned by Pagourzis' father who said he didn't know how his son got them. One witness said Pagourzis had

16. https://en.wikipedia.org/wiki/Santa_Fe_High_School_shooting. Retrieved 5/26/2018.

been bullied by students and coaches. Other than that, there were no obvious red flags and he was known as a quiet student who was "friendly and funny." He was on the honor roll and played on the school football team. Other classmates called him a "weird loner" and said that he "never seemed right."

June 28, 2018.
Capital Gazette, Annapolis, Maryland[17]

Five people were shot dead and two others wounded at the *Capital Gazette* newspaper in Annapolis, Maryland. They were all employees at the newspaper. When the shooter entered the building, he barricaded the back door of the newsroom so people could not escape and set off smoke bombs. He shot through the glass doors of the paper. He used a 12-gauge pump-action shotgun bought legally a year ago. The shooter, Jarrod W. Ramos, age 38, was found hiding under a desk in the newsroom.

Ramos had a long-standing grievance with the paper. In 2011, he pled guilty to harassing a young high school classmate and was sentenced to 90 days in jail. The sentence was suspended by the Judge. Ramos was put on probation, ordered to not contact the woman and to continue getting therapy. Days later, the paper published a detailed account of the crime and following it, Ramos seems to have switched his obsession to the *Gazette.* He filed a defamation lawsuit against the paper the following summer. The lawsuit was dismissed but the threats kept up.

Tom Marquardt, a former executive editor and publisher at the newspaper was fearful that Ramos might be violent against the paper. He said: ". . . this was a guy that was going to come and shoot us. I was concerned on my behalf and on behalf of my staff that he was going to take more than legal action" (Williams and Harman, *The New York Times* 6/29/2018, p. 3). Ramos continued to make threats to the paper over social media that were often violent and profane, but the paper decided not to file charges, hoping not to incite the situation further.

---

17. Information from http://www.msn.com/en-us/annapolis-shooting-suspect-had-long-running -dispute . . . Retrieved 6/29/2018, and http://www.latimes.com/nation/la-na-newspaper-shooting -20180628-story.html. Retrieved 6/29/2018.

July 1, 2018.
Stabbing at Three-Year-Old's Birthday Party, Boise, Idaho[18]

Six children ranging in age from three to 12 were stabbed and three adults were wounded. Many were hospitalized with life-threatening injuries as a result of a rampage at a child's birthday party. The birthday girl died. She was three years old. All were refugees from Syria, Iraq and Ethiopia. The girl who died was Ethiopian. Thirty-year-old Timmy Earl Kinner was arrested for the crime. He had been a temporary resident at the apartment complex where the birthday party was held. The apartment complex caters to low-income families and Kinner lived there until he was asked to leave because of his behavior. He did leave, but returned to enact vengeance. Kinner has a lengthy criminal record in many states.

July 28, 2018.
Shooting in New Orleans Kills Three
People and Wounds Seven Others

Two armed individuals walked up to a group of people outside a strip mall in New Orleans Saturday night wearing hoodies and holding a handgun and a rifle and fired into the assembled crowd, killing two men and one woman and wounding seven more. The strip mall was on a busy street about three miles from the French Quarter. According to law enforcement, one person in the crowd was an intended target of gang violence. The gunmen stood over this person and shot him multiple times. The gunmen are still at large.[19]

August 26, 2018.
Two Shot at Jacksonville, Florida Video Game Tournament

Twenty-four-year-old David Katz, from Baltimore, shot and killed two people and injured 11 others at a Florida video game tournament. Then he killed himself. Katz was participating in a Madden NFL 19 competition at "The Landing" a riverside shopping and dining loca-

---

18. Information from https://www.washingtonpost.com/news/post-nation/wp2018/07/01/boise-stabbing-refugees . . . Retrieved 7/7/2018 and https://www.usatoday.com/story/news/nation/2018/07/03/boise-stabbing-death-birthday-party/754537002/ Retrieved 7/7/2018.

19. https://www.pressherald.com/2018/07/29/mass-shooting-leaves-3-dead-7-wounded-in-new . . . and https://www.businessinsider.com/ap-police-say-3-killed-7-injured-in-new-orleans-shooting. Retrieved 7/31/2018.

tion in Jacksonville, Florida. He was the 2017 winner, but apparently this time got upset over losing the game and opened fire with a handgun. It is unclear whether he knew his victims. He was thought to have a second handgun with him. There are no metal detectors at the entrance to the tournament.

The shooter, David Katz, is known to have a mental illness history. He was psychiatrically hospitalized twice as an adolescent and was prescribed antipsychotic and antidepressant medication when he was 12.

Katz's parents divorced in 2007 when he was about 11. His parents disagreed on how to care for their son and there was a long and bitter custody battle resulting in the mother being awarded custody with visitation for the father. The father, a NASA engineer claimed Katz's mother was exaggerating his mental illness symptoms to win custody. According to Katz's mother (a toxicologist at the Agriculture Department), the father told David not to take his medication. Richard Katz asserted that his ex-wife "had an obsession with using mental health professionals and in particular psychiatric drugs to perform the work that parents should naturally do."[20] Katz began playing video games obsessively as a young adolescent, often refusing to go to school or to bathe.

September 13, 2018.
"Bakersfield Shooting Rampage that Left Six
Dead is 'the New Normal,'" says sheriff[21]

The shootings occurred at multiple locations within a three-mile radius of Bakersfield, California. Javier Cazares, 54 shot his ex-wife and another man at the T & T Trucking Company and then went on to fatally shoot four more people. Finally, he shot himself. The shootings were not thought to be random although the connection to the shooter was unknown. The motive was speculated to be a "domestic violence tragedy." The incident was the third deadliest shooting in the United States in 2018, behind the Marjory Stoneman Douglas High School attack in Florida.

---

20. https://www.cbsnews.com/news/jacksonville-florida-shooting-suspect-madden-tournament . . . Retrieved 8/29/2018.
21. Headline from htpp://w.w.w.msn.com/en-us/news/crime/bakersfield-shooting-rampage-that -left-6-dead-is-the . . . Written by Hannah Fry, Alene Tchekmedyian. Retrieved 9/13/2018/.

September 20, 2018.
Woman Kills Three Plus Herself in Mass Shooting at Pharmacy Warehouse in Aberdeen, Maryland

Four people are dead, including the female shooter, and seven injured after a mass shooting at a Rite Aid pharmacy distribution center in Aberdeen, Maryland outside of Baltimore. The distribution center was believed to be secure. The shooter, Snochia Moseley, age 26, was a temporary worker at the warehouse. She arrived at work about 9 a.m. It was said she was in a "bad mood. She wanted to pick a fight. And then she started shooting."[22] It is very rare for a mass murderer to be a woman.

Comment

If these murderers had been seen and understood, many might have been considered to have given advance notice of murderous rage, clues to serious psychological disturbance and even the potential for violent acting out. Many had serious psychiatric histories. If they had been seen by an astute psychological professional we can hope that less people might be dead. But, in the long run, it remains impossible to predict! Even the most aberrant of behaviors and symptoms don't necessarily lead to violence, and nothing in the known histories of killers, would be able to predict the kind of wanton violence and killing that happened.

If a number of presumed indicators can be collected in hindsight— in the aftermath of a killing—there is likely to be a much higher percentage of people with the same red flags who never actually killed anyone. At this point, we are simply unable to tell the difference and the legal system points toward leniency—especially for white people.

For many decades, mental health laws have protected the civil rights of the individual rather than those of the community. *The Washington Post* reported that "Jonathan Spence, a gunsmith at Guns & Guitars in Mesquite, Nevada where Stephen Paddock [the Las Vegas killer] had purchased weapons said "[I] . . . never found him to be out of the ordinary. He was just like anybody else. Nobody has any answers. It doesn't make sense."[23]

---

22. https://w.w.w.news.com.au/world/north-america/three-dead-in-mas-shooting-in-maryland/ . . . By Emma Reynolds. Retrieved 9/20/2018.
23. Retrieved from the internet, *Washington Post,* November 6, 2017.

Suspected motives for mass murder are listed in droves, from the current propensity and encouragement for acting out in the culture and mental illness, to news media, tv, social media and video games. But one obvious answer in front of our eyes is the easy accessibility of guns. Unique to the United States, an angry person can easily acquire a gun and act out in a way that causes death, perhaps many deaths. Many people, including the current American President, believe that the best way to counteract mass murders is to have a gun yourself. On a morning news program today, I heard the Governor of Texas, twice refuse to answer a gun-restraint question. "People are turning to praying and God and love," he said.

So where does this leave art therapists and other therapists who every day encounter and try to work with acting-out clients? Realistically, in a very difficult, even scary position. To put it bluntly, the practice of art therapy is not only difficult, it is an inherently *dangerous* profession today. Ironically, it seems clear that potential mass murderers who do engage in counseling and therapy, even if they are forced to by the courts, are safer than the ones who remain invisible within the community.

The main message of this book is that the notion that an art therapist or mental health worker, even the most capable one, can predict violence is a fantasy. It is clearly necessary that a realistic appraisal of the situation is an essential part of the art therapist's skill set. But even the most skilled therapist must always carry ambiguity and uncertainly. Still many retain the belief that *we can predict*. Unfortunately, this is simply not true. I wish it were.

Chapter 7

WHY HAVE WE FORGOTTEN THAT CHILDREN SUFFER? A REACTION TO THE MARJORY STONEMAN DOUGLAS HIGH SCHOOL SHOOTING

March 3, 2018

I have been aware for a long time that people seem to forget that, for many, if not most, childhood is not the sunlit, rosy-hued romantic-best-time-of-your life-that-wonderful-time-when you-don't-have-grownup-cares-yet. And I have wondered what causes this forgetting?

Within a context of individual character sensitivities and environmental factors, all children endure some pain growing up and many quite a lot of it. Some are so severely wounded in childhood that as they grow into adolescence and adulthood, they are never able to move past what happened to them. It is these wounds of childhood that as adults, we act out in our day-to-day lives. In Freud's concept of the Repetition Compulsion defense, we endlessly repeat our difficulties because it is what we know, unconsciously hoping that this time the ending will be different. Usually, it isn't.

I have been aware of this apparent forgetfulness in novice therapists, experienced therapists and in teachers and have wondered what it is and why. Is it the inability to look unbearable horrors in the face—those of students, clients or the Self? Is it a compartmentalization of one's own helplessness and suffering so that it is less powerful? Is it repression? I have wondered how a therapist or a teacher could effectively help a child or an adolescent, if they couldn't remember their own pain and, and—without projecting it or overreacting—feel *compassion* and *empathy* for what it is like to be living as a child growing up.

99

Ironically, this suffering is particularly prevalent these days in our violent and chaotic world, where at best, the child has to cope with chaos and fear along with all the rest.

This realization came to the forefront again this week when I heard the latest guardians of Nicklaus Cruz, the Parkland, Florida school shooter, who killed 17 people, mostly students, talking about how respectful and rule-following he was in their home. He gave no clues at all, they said, of the horrors to follow. What they experienced as normalcy was actually terrifically abnormal behavior for Cruz. (It would have been pretty abnormal behavior for even the most "normal" of teenagers, of course.)

As time has gone on, a long, terrible history of red flags have become apparent about Cruz, indicating he had obvious and severe emotional difficulties, combined with an apparent obsession with guns and the access to a number of them. We know he cut himself—a serious symptom of disturbance—and even called 911 to report himself shortly before the shooting. I am not discussing here, the many missed opportunities for intervention and the mistakes made with Cruz. Others will do that. But Nicklaus Cruz was clearly a suffering young man and, I'd guess, he had been in pain for some time.

If all had been well until the following happened, it alone should have been cause enough for serious concern by the people around him: His mother died suddenly from pneumonia four months previous to the Douglas school shooting. The death of a parent at any age, much less childhood, is not something to be "moved on" from.

I once heard a smart therapist say to a child who had recently lost a parent: "You have just experienced the worse thing that can happen to a person!" With her sensitive words, she opened an important conversation about the profound loss that had happened in this child's life and that the child was obviously feeling and attempting to cope with to that time alone. Through her empathic words, the therapist defined how deep the wound was and made it possible for the child to talk about his confusing feelings. And she made it evident that it was important to do so.

Today's culture is a " keep moving on"—simply behave as if everything is okay. There may be so much coming at them, that it can be difficult for a child to even sort out the horror from other everyday occurrences. Looking okay means nobody has to confront what must be obvious childhood suffering underneath. Moving on and looking okay, the adult can believe that it IS okay when it is not. Clearly, it was not in Nicklaus Cruz's case.

Many today have trouble talking about death at all for a whole variety of reasons. People "pass"; they do not die. "Pass" is a gentle way to avoid. Even dogs do not die—they are "put down." To use the word "death" signifies a finality—an end—that "pass" does not. It means "Stop." Stop what you're doing and notice that something huge, something significant has happened—perhaps the most significant and life-changing event that can happen to a person. To say a person "passed" is a usage of language which allows a denial of the tremendous loss and abandonment that has occurred. It ignores the huge bleeding wound needing immediate acknowledgement and attention. A band-aid will not stop this bleeding. It ignores the grievous loss that can finally propel someone over the cliff. It says, "let's move on and ignore." Let us ignore and forget; by ignoring we hope for the best. I wonder if that is what happened to Nik Cruz?

I am reminded of the Jewish word *dayenu*—it would have been sufficient. Whether anyone or anything could have headed off Nicklaus Cruz is a complicated question and cannot be answered here. But it is abundantly clear that from his birth and first days as an adoptive child, to his adoptive father's death 10 years previously, to his adoptive mother's death four months before the monstrous school mass murder, Niklaus Cruz was a boy in pain and in trouble. He came in contact with many adults and friends who knew of his pain. Some were put off by it as "weirdness" and kept their distance. Some kept their distance because that is what they do, when they see something "different" that seems strange to them. But where was the compassion and the action to stop and acknowledge his painful existence and the attempt to heal his horrible wounds of loss? It makes me sad.

Chapter 8

WHAT CAN THE ART THERAPIST DO? PRACTICAL SUGGESTIONS FOR CLINICIANS TO FIND HELP AND SUPPORT IN A DANGEROUS PRACTICE AND CULTURE I: The Safety Landscape in Mental Health

Introduction

On his internet blog, Dr. Ken Pope reviews 66 citations from journal articles and books about occupational danger to mental health workers, in particular psychiatrists and psychologists.[1] In Pope's 2016 book with Melba Vasquez he cites the following statistics from the literature:

- Almost one in every five psychologists reported having been physically attacked by at least one client.
- Over 80% of the psychologists reported having been afraid that a client would attack them.
- Over half reported having had fantasies that a client would attack.
- Over one out of four had summoned the police or security personnel for protection from a client.
- About 3% reported obtaining a weapon to protect themselves . . . (Pope, K. Resources for therapists who are stalked, threatened or attacked by patients, https://kspope.com/stalking.php. Retrieved 11/13/2018.

---

1. https://kspope.com/stalking.php

I am not trying to frighten art therapists, but realistic attention to safety is a more important necessity than it is typically perceived today. Working against great odds, art therapists strive to help their clients function more adequately and to heal. But here is the obvious naked fact: It isn't much help to anyone if the art therapist is killed.

> Violence management must become a critical part of training pro-grams at institutional and professional levels. Acute care educators and clinicians need to discuss violence before it occurs and imple-ment a plan for its management in all inpatient and outpatient set-tings. (Tisher, Gordon and Landry-Meyer, 2000, p. 2)

Some of the following stories about safety (or the lack of it) in public psychiatric institutions and community mental health clinics come from times that no longer exist. In contemporary times, the safety of therapists is definitely better attended to, but it is nowhere near enough. In the dangerous and unpredictable current culture, staff safe-ty must be considered a first priority in mental health.

Research shows that mentally ill people present a greater risk to themselves than to others, if they present a risk at all (Alaszewski, Harrison and Manthorpe, 1998). There is a huge "but" here!: most mass killers are not in therapy and have never been. Most exist unseen and invisible, hidden in the dark, suddenly and dramatically emerging into the light where they murder many and are memorial-ized as tv news video images play over and over again to assault our eyes and break our heart.

Mass murders have always been a part of American life, for exam-ple the slaughter of Native Americans and the lynchings of Black peo-ple. The mass violence that resulted in the killings of thousands of Black people and the recent killings of unarmed Black men have given rise to the Black Lives Matter movement. Then there are the current immigration scandals of separating infants and young children from their parents, which disrupts the developmental attachment process and is very likely to have serious mental health ramifications for decades in these children and could turn them toward violent behav-ior as the grow toward adulthood. Only relatively recently, however, have we had such easy and unregulated access to weapons for killing. Americans seem to have bought into the notion that guns are a constitutional right and there is nothing to be done about it. Have we given up that fight!

The go-to motivation for mass murder these days, even before guns, is mental illness. Is it is easier to "blame" mental illness—undoubtedly a cause—than to take on the wide prevalence and lack of regulation of guns in today's American society? Do we exist in a kind of apathetic malaise neutralized by the gun lobbies to search for other reasons? Undeniably, both guns and mental illness have a part in causation.

Guns and Other Deadly Instruments

It feels like the gun debate has gone on forever propelled by the National Rifle Association (NRA) and the use of the 2nd Amendment of the U.S. Constitution; actually it began only 20 years ago. Now, in a time in which gun violence occurs daily and is ubiquitous, pragmatic steps to inhibit availability and access to guns and to regulate them, in agencies and clinics must be of major importance. Psychiatric clinics and institutions should be gun-free areas with protective devices. These days, it is too easy for a disturbed person to access a gun. Making guns less easily available wouldn't entirely solve the mass murder problem, but it would help.

As I write this, there is a plan announced by Cody Wilson, long-time gun-rights advocate and anarchist, to post plans on the internet for gun-making with a 3-D printer, along with a machine for constructing guns. These plastic guns through a 3-D printer, are illegal because they evade detection by metal detectors and contain no potentially traceable serial numbers. Cody Wilson says "so what!" Publication of plans on the internet would mean that the few regulations about gun ownership and necessary background checks that there are, could be bypassed by "ghost guns." Republican Senator Mike Rounds of South Dakota said "this is new technology which you're not going to put back into the bottle. It is there.[1] Cody Wilson has pushed for publishing gun plans since his days as a student at the University of Texas, citing his First Amendment rights. He founded the non-profit company Defense Distributed to publish the plans. A few weeks ago, the State Department reversed an Obama-era ruling prohibiting Wilson's plan, that has effectively cleared the path for "Mr.

---

1. Ibid.

Wilson to usher in what his website calls 'the age of the downloadable gun'."[2]

Critics say that the publication of 3-D printed weapons is a threat to public safety. Supporters say it's a First Amendment right. Attorneys-general in eight states and the District of Columbia filed a joint lawsuit against the Trump administration attempting to prevent Wilson from publishing the plans online. A Seattle federal judge issued a temporary nationwide injunction saying the lawyers bringing suit had established "a likelihood of irreparable harm"[1] blocking the publication for the time being, but only "temporarily" and my guess is, not forever. Wilson planned to publish his plans anyway. His lawyers said "This is a huge free speech case. They compared it to the Pentagon Papers case in which the Supreme Court rejected the government's attempts to block new organizations from publishing a secret history of the Vietnam War.[3] I am told that at the gun store on south Whidbey Island where I live, after a mass murder, gun sales go up, because buyers are afraid the government is about to take guns away. Easy access to guns in America is an obvious cause of the incipient virus of gun violence and mass murder: "America has been experimenting . . . for decades. The results are exactly as you would expect. Mass gun ownership leads to higher rates of gun death. Careful regulation can limit that death toll, but not eliminate it.[4] (Ladd, C. October 6, 2017).

According to statistics, actually crime *has been declining* for decades, but the nexus between gun ownership and gun deaths is "unavoidably linear."[5] Ladd (October 6, 2017) writes: "guns are now competing with automobile accidents for one of the leading causes of premature death in the U.S." For a person feeling a twinge of anger or revenge, a gun is readily available and a gun is much more dangerous instrument than anything else for killing. Most mass murders, though not all, concern guns. In addition, many shooters have an arsenal of numerous guns. Some politicians advocate putting *more* guns in places like schools as a solution to the killing problem. Guns in the hands of

1. Ibid.
2. Shear, M., Hsu, T. & Johnson, K. (July 31, 2018.) https://www.nytimes.com/2018/o7/31/us/politics/3-d- guns-trump-html. Retrieved 8/8/2018.
3. Ibid.
4. Ladd, C. (October 6, 2017). "Ten lies distort the gun control debate." https://www.forbes.com /sites/chrisladd/2017/10/06/ten-lies-distor-the-gun-control-debate/ Retrieved 8/7/2016.
5. Ibid.

"good" people instead of "bad" people would act as an effective deterrent, they say. Ladd (2017) suggests that existing gun laws "are carefully crafted to be unenforceable":

> One law stands out as the most critical obstacle of enforcement of gun restrictions. A minor provision of the 1986 Firearm Owners Protection Act bans states or federal agencies from building gun registration

> Congress has protected gun companies from lawsuits. Threats from the NRA have blocked the Centers for Disease Control from researching gun deaths. State and federal laws block law enforcement officials from effectively tracking weapons used in crimes. . . . Americans now have more guns in circulation than citizens. (October 6, 2017)

Immediately after a mass shooting, the initial response to mass shooting is an outcry for gun control. Action is demanded. Petitions are signed and donations given. Time moves on and we are left with no change, and little but prayers and thoughts. Even after the dramatic and horrible shooting in the New Town elementary school in which 20 children and seven adults were killed, it proved impossible to get tighter gun laws passed by the United States legislature. President Obama approved 23 executive actions and proposed 12 proposals for Congress. These proposals were opposed by the NRA and other pro-gun groups and were largely defeated. At the state level, five states passed stricter gun laws, while ten states passed laws weakening firearm restrictions.

When I was growing up, there was the Cold War. Fear of nuclear attack led to school drills with students hiding under their desks. Today, school shootings have become such a regular occurrence that after the Parkland School shooting, in which seventeen were killed, the students of Marjory Stoneman Douglas High School were called "members of the mass shooting generation." But they said "enough is enough" and began to demonstrate and speak out. Alex Wind, a student survivor at Parkland told *60 Minutes:* "We are the generation that's had to be trapped in closets, waiting for police to come or waiting for a shooter to walk in to our door. . . . We are the people that know what it's like firsthand" (Vasilogambros, M., 8/22/18). Because of their resistance and opposition, an incredibly successful year for the gun control movement in the United States began. States enacted fifty new laws restricting gun access.[6]

Safety in the Physical Plant

Some years back, as Director of an art therapy program in a university in Los Angeles, I went to visit two clinics to evaluate them as potential internship sites for our graduate students. This was soon after a social worker had been shot to death in an outpatient clinic in L.A., although neither of the clinics I visited were where it had happened. I remember the stark contrast: To enter the first clinic was like entering a jail. Whatever kind of building it had once been, when I saw it, all three stories were covered with metal bars and locked gates. In order to enter the first floor, and every floor thereafter, I needed to phone someone inside, identify myself and the someone inside would electronically open the gate for me to enter. Then I would do it all over again to get through the next door or to the next floor. I remember the sound of the clanging gates behind me, like a prison. The second clinic I visited looked more like a suburban house that could have had a family living inside (which earlier, it probably was.) It had no bars whatsoever. I entered the unlocked front door into a reception room where I identified myself to a woman sitting at a desk, behind an open glass window. After a short time sitting in the outer room with what apparently were waiting clients, I was ushered into the back by a staff member. This clinic and its inhabitants would have made an easy target for a shooter.

Safety, and the Lack of it, for Art Therapy Clinicians

I learned that a graduate student I supervised was holding sessions with what she believed was a potentially violent client on Sundays at the clinic where she was alone in the building without even an administrative assistant or custodian there. She didn't know how inappropriate that was. It was only through my direct questioning, that this dangerous fact emerged because the student, herself, didn't have any idea it might be a problem. An art therapy clinician I supervised, two or three years post masters in private practice, was seeing a woman who

---

6. It should be noted, however, that ten states managed to pass laws expanding access to guns, ranging from arming K-12 staff to supporting Stand Your Grounds laws.

had a dangerous domestic violence history. The wife had managed to leave the home with her children for a women's shelter and was now embattled in a bitter legal custody battle with her ex-husband.

Research shows that this period is a particularly crucial time for violence to occur to the woman and to the therapist, because the ex has realized he no longer has control over his partner. This art therapist had her practice in a general office building, was seeing her client at 6 p.m. after most other inhabitants of the building had gone home and was generally alone in the building with her client. After the session, regularly, she locked up her office and the building and walked to her car in the parking lot two floors below. The art therapist refused to acknowledge the very real potential of danger and refused to take steps at all to take care of herself. As her supervisor, I was terrified for her and angry at her refusal to care for herself. I struggled with my vision of her shot dead in the parking lot. Luckily, this didn't happen! Another story: A few years ago, having an appointment with school personnel to talk over a project, I walked in the unlocked front door of the school and went directly to the office. In these times, this should be as shocking as it was to me.

After the Virginia Tech massacre where 32 people were murdered, and the killer had a long documented mental illness history including serious questions raised by his professors, I believed that mental health clinics everywhere would take the dramatic and unfortunate murder as an obvious opportunity to go over safety measures with staff. If they already had a safety plan in place, they would bring it to the forefront, making staff again aware of the potential of danger. If they didn't have a safety plan, they would create one, I thought. But I was naive: from what I learned, most didn't.

Safety Orientation in Art Therapy Education Programs[7] and in Job Orientation

That being an art therapist and that the profession of art therapy are innately dangerous at all times, but especially these, does not seem to have reached the current curriculum of graduate programs at all. That an art therapist strives to keep *the client* safe *is* taught in required

---

7. Information and quotes in this section are from an informal safety survey of art therapy clinicians conducted by the author from different parts of the country and in different mental health settings. Identifying information is omitted.

ethics classes, where suicidality, danger to self and others and the therapist's duty to warn are reviewed as ethical and legal codes, but the
physical safety of the therapist is not.

"Self Care" is a typical topic in graduate training programs these
days. But Self Care is usually focused on measures the art therapist
can take to keep herself from burnout and general malaise. It is
assumed that working with clients is difficult and that the art therapist
needs to care for herself too. This attention to Self Care in graduate
art therapy programs and the profession of art therapy enhances an
individualized incentive for the trainee and the experienced therapist
to be able to carry on doing the work and it shifts any responsibility
from the agency to the art therapist. It accepts what is and doesn't
pose questions to mental health or clinic systems or their safety for the
art therapist.

Safety in Mental Health Clinics and Institutions Today

To gather recent data about clinic safety practices, I conducted a
small nationwide survey with art therapists. A therapist who works in
public schools reported:

> [At the agency, I received] no safety orientation ever.. I am often the
> initial person to assess . . . for danger to self or others. . . . Panic but-
> ton sure would be nice . . . many clinicians are either hired by
> schools or sent there by outside agencies. This is a real issue as you
> can see by the frequent school shootings that occur.

According to my art therapist informants, in-patient hospitals,
where many patients are known to be dangerous seem to have the
best safety training for staff. One art therapist writes:

> . . . Some of the clients were very violent. I received a great deal of
> excellent training on physical restraint of client and safety measures
> (verbal de-escalation and physical evasion mostly).

And another:

> [Before I started the job] I received some weeks of orientation,
> including 8–10 hours of safety training much of which was hands-on
> and taught by a designated emergency response team. . . . My under-

standing of what exists now was that it is primarily a result of gun violence in the hospital in which a number of people were killed and wounded.

But in outpatient clinics:

> There was not a discussion during my orientation to the job, regarding my own safety. . . . We did bring up safety after I did an intake with a verbally aggressive individual who had walked in off the street. He had several bags with him and talked about firearms. We then created a code word for when we feel unsafe with a client and took some safety-in-the-workplace trainings online.

Locking the Doors

On the plus side, an art therapist working in an in-patient hospital wrote:

> The hospital has it's own police force and a designated trained security force. Not only are the units locked, the hospital entrance itself has 24-hour guards, key card access, video cameras and metal detectors. Staff members with direct client contact are issued a device which audibly alerts responders on the floor and sends a GPS location to the security office.

But outpatient community clinics are more varied:

> There are two doors which are generally unlocked. One is in the back of the building and easily accessible to anyone who wants to enter.

> My clinic has locked doors at all times. People must be buzzed in.

> Clinicians are scheduled so that if there are late hours, more than one is present at any given time. We have had walk-in clients some of whom have prompted us to call the police. Fortunately, the local police department has been highly cooperative at such times and once remained here for several hours until a determination was made as to what to do with the client.

> Most of my work is in a domestic violence program . . . there are several domestic violence victims whose boyfriends/husbands continue

to stalk them. This has put several staff members in jeopardy. We don't allow abusers into the building since it's a safe place for victims.

The following day, this same art therapist, upset by an incident, wrote the following:

> . . . so I had to call the Child Abuse hotline today and I know the mom will figure out who called and that makes me feel unsafe. . . . If her abuser woos her back, then he will be on my trail as well and he's a son of a bitch. I think my note to you yesterday made it seem like there's not much danger. There is!

And this:

> The door is unlocked from 9-5. If we have walk-in slots and same-day service available for clients, we can get a boost in funding. It is a numbers game. We have two entrances. One does not go by the front desk person. It would be easy for someone to enter there unannounced and unseen.

To Repeat

Can violence be predicted? No. Can violence be predicted by interpreting violent imagery in artwork? No. Can violence be predicted from art therapy imagery by a skillful and experienced art therapist? No. Are mental health clinics and institutions consciously caring for the safety of staff? No.

Chapter 9

WHAT CAN THE ART THERAPIST DO? PRACTICAL SUGGESTIONS FOR CLINICIANS TO FIND HELP AND SUPPORT IN A DANGEROUS PRACTICE AND CULTURE II: Applications

Introduction

There is required planning for cities and communities about fire, hurricanes and other disasters. Public schools have safety drills to prepare students for mass shooters—Marjorey Stoneman Douglas High School in Parkland, ironically, had regular drills and was seemingly well prepared. We know that when the fire alarm goes off, we evacuate the building. Where I live, there are road signs directing an automobile route away from a coming tsunami. All too often, however, staff safety is not anywhere in the forefront of mental health systems, agencies and clinics. Sometimes it is not even mentioned.

Safety Should be Integral to Art Therapy Practice

Safety for art therapy practitioners should be an active focus of contemporary clinic life and practice. Without being melodramatic or over-reactive, it is urgent that the agency be pro- active in its' safety planning and procedures. Safety practices should be folded into a clinic's regular processes and procedures. Mental health institutions today work hard to protect clients. Staff and therapists, not so much so far.

Safety practices should be an integral and habitual part of job orientation, discussed openly periodically and regularly. Staff members in a mental health agency or institution should know about the history of violence in their specific clinic, how to protect themselves and what the backup for them and their client is when they feel fearful. Art therapy practitioners are often on the front line in their work with clients. In any conflict between confidentiality and danger to the therapist, safety wins out. In addition, senior staff has the responsibility to help junior staff deal with their fears and dangerous situations. While the unsettling nature of this work is that is inherently unpredictable, attention must be paid and acute awareness developed by the art therapy clinician and by the agency.

Safety must be a living and active part of any clinic's fabric. Staff fear must be openly addressed. To ignore the realities and uncertainties of clinical practice is, I believe, unethical, dangerous and downright stupid. I am no lawyer but I believe it is probably a bad idea legally as well.

About Risk Assessment for Psychiatric Clinics and Institutions

There are many risk assessment protocols available these days (even on the internet) to help the facility assess and improve its site safety and the safety of its clients and staff. Nevertheless, it is important to recognize that whatever safety mechanisms and procedures may be in place, the facility can never be wholly safe—and that should be part of the reality equation too. Risk can be minimized by good communication, attention to staff and client safety and appropriate planning. But risk can never be eliminated entirely. Still, we need to do better. Our lives and our client's lives may depend on it.

Evaluating a Client: Red Flags

[research has shown] that the best predictor of future aggression is a history of past aggression. (Sandberg, McNiel and Binder, 1998)

The best predictor of future behavior is past behavior—sometimes. We can never be certain, but we can and should, become familiar with clues. At beginning contact with the agency, the intake worker and art therapist must have a keen awareness of important information which may provide clues alerting to a threat of violence.[1] This information

---

1. In the first session, the clinician must search out these clues. To count on the intake worker or another clinician taking "care of it" is foolish and dangerous.

may come from the client him or herself, from the presenting problem, from previous clinical files, from relevant contacts with professionals or any or all of the above. But, caution: Having specific information about a client is no guarantee of future violence or not. The milieu of any form of mental health work is the art therapists' ability to live within the reality of *not knowing* and of *never knowing for sure.* Recognizing danger signs and the occurrence of any or all of the following characteristics in a client, *at any time* should make the hackles go up on a therapist's neck and should send her or him to seek support and guidance from a senior clinician, alerting backup and perhaps even the authorities and warning essential others. It is the art therapist's ethical responsibility to act in a professional manner to protect the community, the therapist, the client and the agency from harm. Sometimes the art therapist may think she/he should be able to "handle anything." This is a fantasy that novice art therapists are particularly prone to. Sometimes there is shame or embarrassment about asking for help. Even if one thinks they might be overreacting, DON'T STAY SILENT!

Following are some red flags:

- **In the History:** Previous violence,[2] behavioral acting out in the living environment or the community, conduct disorder, or non-compliance with treatment and/or medications.
- **In the Clinical Presentation:** Command hallucinations, manic phase of bipolar disorder, impulse control (including self-harm behaviors, history of or intentions,) drug or alcohol use/problems.
- **In the Presentation of Self:** Anger, emotional control problems, impulsivity, low frustration tolerance, anti-social beliefs or behavior.
- **In the Context/Environment:** Little or no stability or support from family, history of trauma, broken family/friend/child relationships age/ethnicity/gender: many violent offenders are young white men between the ages of 15–40.

---

2. Some of this information is culled from "Assessing the Risk of Violence," https://www.hse.ie /edg/sciences/publications/mental/health/risk. Risk management in mental health services. Feidheannacht na Seirbhise, Slaiute Health Service Executive. Retrieved 7/18/2018.

Evaluating the Art Therapist's Expectations and Limitations

In the last years, I have supervised and mentored a number of art therapists who were in graduate educational programs and later in their first years and first jobs after graduation. The chaos of contemporary life today is unfortunately reflected in an overworked and underpaid mental health system, which can be hardly be a comfortable, safe "home" for the helpers and all-too-often doesn't work well for those they serve either—the clients.

Education to be an art therapist is expensive and many art therapists finish school with financial debts. They need to begin to make money immediately after their years of education so, as quickly as possible and as soon as they can get a job, they enter into what is the mental health system pressure cooker. Workers typically are overloaded with huge caseloads of seriously wounded clients. No one goes to a therapist these days to resolve a relatively simple problem of living; they cannot afford to. Many of today's chronic clients have been in the mental health system for years and have had multiple therapists. Many clients today have devastating traumas and abuse histories which began at birth or in early childhood. Thirty years ago, a suicidal client in one's caseload tended to be a fairly rare occurrence. Today, suicide has become a virus, especially among teenagers, and hardly a week goes by that a therapist does not have to deal with the frightening and now common problem called "suicidal ideation"— which means that the client has been considering suicide and may have specific plans to carry it out. Recently graduated art therapists immediately encounter huge real-world, life and death problems that often have little to do with what they may have learned in their "clean," idealized ivory tower education.

Some years ago, I heard a very fine therapist, receiving a prestigious award, say it took her seven years before she "knew what she was doing." Leaving school and entering into the "real world," art therapists work within an onslaught while they are at their most vulnerable and still in need of plenty of support and teaching. They are learning their way and will be for a number of years. Given their financial situations, they may cut corners and not seek out the supportive supervision they need, making an already dangerous situation more dangerous. Confronted with intractable and long-term client problems and admitted pressure and confusion, they may even blame themselves. They should know the right thing to do or if they could come up with exactly the right directive it would all go well. With intractable and difficult client issues that would take a seasoned therapist a long time to help (if it were at all possible,) many art therapists may believe it is *their* problem if things do not go well. A good supervisor could help sort this out, but given shrinking budgets, often they are not available to the fledgling art therapist within the agency. Or perhaps the poor therapist has chosen this as the unfortunate place to cut financial corners and is left feeling alone.

Art therapists and other mental health practitioners are not gods who can make the rock move up the hill. They are humans with inherent limitations and expectations possibly completely out of line with the realities. White privilege, for example, is something that many therapists are not aware of, since even today white, all too often in mental health, is the assumed norm. (Cf. journal articles.) On the other hand, making assumptions about people of color may be just as erroneous.

Our limitations and expectations are hard-wired into us, wrought by our environmental context, reflective of who we are, our education and of the assumptions we consciously and unconsciously carry. Too many therapists may not recognize this fact. Not being aware of one's naturally occurring limitations may make possible the denial of realistic danger when it does occur.

What Might be Some Limitations?

Who the art therapist is: The personal characteristics of the therapist are likely to elicit the client's projections, having an impact on and meaning for the therapy.

- **Gender:** I am a woman, not a man.
- **Age:** I am a woman of a certain age, not a 20 year old.
- **Ethnicity:** One's ethnicity has meaning.
- **Color and Race:** Ditto
- **Language:** Accents may elicit client feelings.
- **Experience:** Having had a family and raised children, I can better understand the nuances of this difficult endeavor. I have had other experiences during my life which help me understand the existential struggles of what my client might be going through. But there are some situations I can not understand. Here, the client is often the best teacher.

Limits and Referring

There are certain kinds of clients, I will not see—a Nazi, ex-Nazi or White Supremacist for example and perhaps not a pedophile. If I have a client who is impossible for me, a referral to another therapist is needed. It is ethical and professional to refer a client that you would be biased against. It would never be to the client's advantage to be working with a therapist who could not like them and be able to feel empathic.

I am not inferring that every limitation is an indication that the therapist must refer the client. Many therapist limitations can be overcome through awareness, empathy, compassion and education. But there are some that cannot. I suggest that the art therapist with a question about this see the client twice and if the therapist can't work with the client, a referral to another therapist is necessary. Probably a discussion with a senior staff person is in order first. What I am saying is that the therapist must be conscious of personal limitations and do some honest soul searching, about who they are, what their limits are and how this is likely to impact the therapeutic relationship.

The Uses of Humor

Seldom mentioned and little researched are the effects of humor on the client and on the therapist. I want to mention it here as a fundamental skill for the therapist. Not every therapist has an active sense of humor, but it can be developed. Laughter can provide relief and "time out" from apparently insurmountable problems. Obviously, I am not suggesting that the art therapist spend the time cracking jokes and, you say, there is nothing funny about this business. "Trying to help people is the most serious endeavor there is," and "there is nothing funny about suffering." I consider humor an essential alleviating element in therapy. It eases intensity and potential burnout for the therapist. For the client, it can break the hold of pain and confusion which can be an immense relief—if only for a short while. There are myriad ways humor can be used in therapy, but I have found that the most difficult thing can be said to the client if it is said with humor.

In art therapy, humor can be used to ease pain by "turning the tables" for example and asking the client to make a silly or funny picture. The process of "reframing" is a creative act in which the problem is turned into something positive and unexpected. "We fight all the time," says the family. "At least you're in the ring together," says the therapist.

Expectations and Change

Every therapist carries a set of expectations that are part of their own personal makeup arising from background and experience. It is important that the therapist recognize expectations in herself, so that they can be modulated to appropriately fit the client.

An erroneous expectation held by many art therapists is about *change*. The therapist assumes if a client comes to therapy they want to change. Yes and no. Sometimes a client comes to therapy to NOT change. Change is an enormously complicated mechanism, never straight forward and one we do not much understand. It's unconscious layers are like the layers of a decades-old mountain, with ancient fissures that are largely invisible. No doubt, the client wants to do better, but there may be a vast reservoir—personal, interpersonal and cultural—which inhibits effective change or even prohibits it altogether.

The art therapist's expectations about change affect treatment. If the therapist expects too much change, the client can only disappoint and fail the therapist and her or himself. If a therapist expects that the client change too quickly, there may only be gigantic disappointment when this doesn't happen. I have often heard novice therapists claim a "breakthrough" with their client after a short time. This is ridiculous. It can be understood as the therapist's need to see change where probably none exists. It can reflect the therapist's denial and wish for control. If a therapist believes that *they* are finally the one who can help the client make change where others could not—look out!

After many decades of practice, I believe that people don't change much. Two stories about expectations:

1. Research shows that students can be more effective than experienced therapists because they don't know what they can't do, so they do it.
2. A very frustrated therapist said to her client "you're such a smart woman; I don't know why you won't do what I suggest."

     The woman came to the next session having made a number of the suggested changes. The therapist asked why the woman had changed. She said, "No one ever called me smart before!"

Holding the Hope

Beginning therapy, a client is desperate and hopeless. They have tried everything they knew to do, maybe for a long time, and none of it has worked. They enter into therapy feeling diminished and defeated. But that they come at all indicates that despite what it looks like, the flame of hope has not entirely been extinguished. There is still a tiny hope. The therapist now holds the client's hope, like a lamp, until the client can take it back. On the doorstep, a client hopes the art therapist can do something, anything, to ease their suffering. Consciously or unconsciously, they wish for the proverbial "magic wand" to eliminate the pain. It should be fast too, they think. Part of what the therapist must do in the early stages of therapy, is conquer the magic wand fantasy while still maintaining the possibility of change. The art therapist must create more realistic expectations for the client and the beginning of that is that the art therapist understand and manage their own expectations.

In the realm of expectations, an art therapist, like other therapists, must examine her/his unconscious assumptions about hope. Are you hopeful that there is at least some possibility that things will be better? You say: "Well, of course I am. Why would I have chosen this field if I didn't believe in hope?" Wait a minute—it's not so simple. I once met a person training to be a mental health clinician. In his depths, he felt absolutely hopeless about people. Are you a glass half-full kind of person? Or are you a glass half empty one? Be honest: If you feel hopeless, it will affect the work you do. And if you feel hopeless about people, you might need to get into another business.

In the darkest times a good therapist must feel and exhibit a sense of *hope* for the future, a profound conviction that things can improve for human lives. Without hope, the art therapist cannot be effective and worse, may even cause damage. Covering up hopelessness with behavioral and cognitive therapies doesn't work either. Hope is an essential and necessary tool of therapy. If my therapist does not believe that things can get better, how can I believe it myself? If the therapist has lost the sense of hope, even for awhile, or is immune to human misery, ethically she may need to step aside for awhile. If a therapist feels hopeless, to put it bluntly, she should seek other work or take a long vacation.

The therapist holds the hope, like a light. Dim, and hardly visible, in the therapist's hands, the light of hope does not go out until the client can pick it up and carry it again. Stanley Crouch, poet, music, jazz and cultural critic wrote: "The belief that the people will get it right eventually . . . that is the hope."

Empathy

It seems too obvious to mention, but EMPATHY is an essential and necessary skill for the art therapist. Recent research asserts that empathy cannot be trained. I disagree, but good therapy can't be done without it. Technical skills are important, but relationship skills are even more important. The art therapist has to be able to skillfully open to the other to understand their existential world as best as they can. Ironically, it this basic ability of empathizing that takes a toll on the therapist and it tends to get worse over time.

Doing therapy requires a stance of *giving,* of helping the other person. Therapy is always for the client, not the therapist and if the art therapist stays open, as they should, they are pretty sure to become depleted eventually. I have seen therapists become so overcome and exhausted that they had trouble functioning at all. The I- can-do-everything attitude is not useful to the therapist nor to the client. Being aware of your needs. Knowing your personal and professional limitations are essential therapist functions in the calling of art therapy.

There is also what is called "compassion fatigue." Watch for it. "Compassion fatigue" describes a condition the therapist suffers. This is what it is: A therapist standardly confronts much personal suffering and difficult emotional material from their clients. At some point it will get to the "too much" point. A therapist hardly ever hears anything positive—that is the nature of the work. Within this context of pain, the art therapist needs to be acutely cognizant of her own needs. Part of the pleasure of being an art therapist is the permission and necessity to be self aware. Part of the problem of art therapy is deciding what to do when that self-awareness indicates a change.

Transitioning

When the system treats the therapist and clients as robots, it is as if there was never any meaning or relationship there. Both therapist and client feel less than human and, if it existed, hope evaporates. There are clients who are transferred to the next therapist as if therapists and clients were some impersonal, bureaucratic, forgettable cog in the system. It is a major task of the therapist to treat the client as a human being. While this sounds obvious and like common sense, it is not. Some clients may be shifted from intern to intern as a matter of course in an agency and without even acknowledgement and this "transitioning" can go on for years. A transition from one therapist to another is a *loss* for the client. When transition happens without acknowledgement, the prevailing message is that comings and goings are not important. I believe they *are* important, that they are reflective of past abandonments in the client's life and, as such may be the most important material there is in therapy.

Contemprary Culture and Its Impact

For many, the Trump era is an age of anxiety and despair. A prevailing cultural hopelessness and depression affects many, including our clients and ourselves. It often makes us feel helpless at our apparent lack of control and through a kind of osmosis, infects our life as a clinician. The cultural mood and zeitgeist today *are* depressing. A reflection can be seen in the proliferation in popular culture of doomsday, dystopian and apocalyptic material and the popularity of back-from-the-dead zombies. Humans are to blame, they say. There is a focus on killings and an unbridled attraction to guns including the mass murders discussed in this book. It is impossible for us to feel everything as it flashes across the repeating images of television and social media we have become addicted to, and that we have let into our houses and our dreams, like a terroristic intruder. Drugs offer escape but lead into darkness. Suicide, once a desperate measure for a few, is a more acceptable answer for many more. Even the environmental movement is about potential death. "Save the planet" means without thoughtful intervention to ward off the effects of human presence, the planet will die.

Some believe the reasonable way to continue on is to become deadened or dead. Current thinkers, philosophers and writers point to damaging and disruptive characteristics of social media, technology and the digital age in which things come so fast that human physiology doesn't have time to adapt. People may feel a constant sense of disease, exhaustion and of being bombbarded. The elusive notion of "balance" has disappeared along with "truth." Subterranean, it exists in the anger bubbling up in unexpected places—like road rage. Do we need to numb ourselves and become something less than human to continue on? What's the way out? What could be a way forward?

Protecting the Art Therapist

The Truism that Imagery is Predictive?

The power of the image to be predictive is a usual truism in art therapy practice. It is believed by many that artwork may contain predictive meaning that even the client is not consciously aware of but that the therapist can see. There is little truth to this supposition and in the era of mass murders and shootings, is an outdated idea.

As an externalization of internal processes, imagery depicting aggressive violence, particularly gun violence should immediately alert the art therapist that something important is going on. Nevertheless, art work can never be counted on to be predictive of future action. Consider the artwork of imprisoned serial killers, which in general is disturbing, strange and violent and compare it to the deeply depressed and ineffectual imagery of serial killer Eric Leonard who was convicted of shooting six people and is now on Death Row (see Chapter 4). Both kinds of imagery turns out to be made by killers.

Violence in imagery, intention and behavior is unpredictable and can erupt abruptly. But there *are* red flags that must not be ignored and the art therapist should never be lulled into denial. Some years ago, when I was a professor at Loyola Marymount University, a student in my class received a serious death threat from a client in her clinical internship. He vowed he would come on campus and shoot her. In class, this predicament was announced to the other students and the threatened student was seated in the center of the classroom to provide her some protection if her client entered. I alerted campus security and described the client. Security would try to stop this person at the kiosk entrance to the university if he appeared. I taught the class that day while two security officers with guns patrolled outside the class. I watched them through the windows walking back and forth. Nothing happened, but any threat is to be taken seriously. The reality and security measures taken to protect the art therapy student was an exceptionally good lesson for the other students.

There *are* red flags that the therapist should be aware of, concerned about and take steps to plan for. But they present a tricky conundrum indeed, evoking serious professional and ethical conflicts about confidentiality and client's rights versus the safety of the therapist. There is no question, however: *The safety of the therapist is the first priority.* The following list is a reminder of current issues. Much of it seems like common sense. Unfortunately, it is not.

- You should be aware that the calling of art therapy IS a dangerous profession.
- In advance, you should be knowledgeable about the general clinic safety plan, including building exits and security. If not a part of job orientation, ASK!
- You should be knowledgeable about consulting room safety.
- If you become concerned about a client, or yourself, a senior staff person should be alerted.
- Don't be embarrassed to ask for help. Asking for help when necessary is a basic skill that many a therapist needs to learn, particularly novices. Therapy is too difficult to do alone.
- Perhaps authorities should be alerted.
- Take any threat seriously. If a homicidal threat is made, you have a legal duty to warn the person or person's threatened.
- Is there a panic button in the room? (Should there be?)
- Should you be sitting near the door?
- Should you have another staff person in the room?
- Should security be alerted?
- Should you have a session with the client at all?
- The art therapist can play a crucial leadership role as an advocate for safety.

Physical and Mental Health of the Art Therapist

Taking Care of Yourself

Clients deserve a healthy, capable therapist. The therapist is like an athlete. They must be protective of themselves and be as fit as possible to do their best work. Watch champion Serena Williams on the tennis court. She has a whole team to help her play her best including a physical therapist, a psychologist, a coach and others that travel from tournament to tournament with her. Obviously, therapists do not have teams to care for them. Too bad. They must be sure to "take their own temperature" regularly and use necessary steps to *nurture themselves*. Self-monitoring should be an essential and regular act for one's whole career. Along with the positive things about being an art therapist, it is inherently tough and exhausting. Watch out for stress symptoms, like having trouble sleeping. What helps a therapist "fill up" when she finds herself overcome, is different from one to the other. An "empty" art therapist is not a good one.

Some Suggestions:

- Hire a supervisor or consultant. You might need your own therapist. You need another to talk things over with and to support you. Do not do this with friends! They have their own axes to grind.
- Form a peer group of colleagues that meets monthly to offer support and information. You would be doing your colleagues a favor along with taking care of yourself.
- Develop and nurture an active outside life. Pay attention to family.
- Re-assess scheduling to give yourself more time.
- Schedule pleasurable activities.
- Learn to say NO.
- Do something that feels good to you. Get into nature. Sit under a tree or take a hike. Or do nothing for awhile.
- Should you do your own art? As you probably know, there are many art therapists that recommend this. It doesn't work for me. If it helps you, do it. If not, don't.
- Read about your work. Acquire more intellectual knowledge about clients, their diagnoses and their troubles. Go to conferences for friendship and learning.
- Take up physical and spiritual endeavors like yoga, meditation or massage and do them regularly.
- LAUGH. Do whatever it takes to get your mind off your work. See laugh-out-loud movies. Read funny books. See stand-up comedians. Become a stand-up comedian. Develop a humorous take on life. Research has shown that humor helps physiologically.
- Take a vacation.
- Take a *long* vacation.

Chapter 10

DANGERS AND THE CALLING
OF ART THERAPY

Growing up with a deaf mother, I learned to listen for what was said and what was not said, presence and absence, noise and silence. As an artist, it was important to me that my art say something. As an art therapist, training and experience taught that what was missing from the image might be more important than what could be seen. I learned to see and hear what was said and what was not said, surface and depth, dark and light. To be able to "see" what is absent is a crucial skill for a therapist.

I pay attention to the reactions I get when I am writing a book. With this one, I usually experienced a quick distancing from the subject. I was asked if I am a serial killer (seriously) and there was a definite, if covert indication that my interest in mass murders and murderers might make me a bit mentally unstable myself. In the more than three years it has taken me to write this book, reactions have been largely absent. Except for some huffs and puffs about what an awful subject mass murders is, there has been a noticeable lack of verbal reaction and a prolonged silence about my work. Perhaps we have here an interesting window into the almost immediate avoidance of danger in current culture—the magical thinking of "if we do not see, it does not exist." Yet there is fascination with the "odd" as well.

I looked for previous research and literature in the area and was surprised to find little or none. Why? For mass murders and mass shootings, it could be speculated that it may be early to have much yet, even though mass murders now seem an everyday occurrence and despite this almost daily increase, mass murders and serial killings have actually been going on for a long time. As I prepared to write the section in this book on serial killers, I looked for literature on the art of serial killers and found nothing. Instead, I discovered the huge industry of "murderabilia"—pages and pages on the internet in which objects owned by or made by serial killers, including their art, are offered for sale to collectors for huge sums of money. It is said that George Zimmerman's gun[1] was recently sold for $250,000!

My mass murders artwork (Chapter 5) has been disquieting, even disturbing to those I know. A friend's reaction was: "It's very interesting, but I wouldn't like to hang it over my couch." I didn't try to exhibit any in the local galleries which need to sell art to stay in business. But in the Fine Arts section at the Island County Fair my mass murders artwork won "Best in Show" and I received a huge blue ribbon. My artwork was exhibited next to the usual benign paintings of farm animals, cows and dogs. How is any of this to be explained?

Language is a good indicator of social and cultural values and I have noticed the word "comfortable" being used a lot these days. "Are you comfortable with that?" or "I am not comfortable with that,"—a lack of comfort often meaning "stay away." "Appropriate" is another overused word. "Appropriate" means there is a right and wrong way to do something and a *rule* about what is right. Why have being "comfortable" and being "appropriate" become so prominent in our language? Might they have to do with avoiding societal danger? These words imply that there is a correct homeostasis or balance. While it might be an unhealthy balance, nonetheless it is a balance. But to maintain balance at all costs is to avoid change. To remain "comfortable" *is to avoid change.*

Change requires taking a risk, stepping off the comfortable curb and away from the familiar into an unknown abyss. The aim of therapy is to provide a support system, a safety net if you will, so that the client is able to leave the known and take that risk to do something better. There is nothing "comfortable" about change. Anger often fuels change and without it, change can be unlikely. The emphasis on staying comfortable and appropriate can make change more difficult, perhaps impossible altogether. Or is the reaching for comfort a desperate need for a safe place against societal change that is coming too fast?

---

1. In 2012, George Zimmerman was acquitted of shooting to death Trayvon Martin a seventeen-year-old African American high school student. As a defense he used Florida's "stand your ground" law.

I asked a number of art therapist clinicians about safety in their work places and, in particular, about safety measures for therapists. My own experiences were some years ago and I hoped that things had progressed. They have, but there are two major lacks today worth mentioning: First, almost all thinking about safety and safety measures is directed *toward the client not the therapist.* Second, safety as a crucial issue for a therapist *does not seem to be taught in graduate art therapy educational programs.* Such things as mandated reporting and duty to warn about clients are taught and self-care for art therapists is mentioned. However, that a student or novice is entering into the calling of art therapy—which is to embark on an innately dangerous profession— seems not to be generally acknowledged in graduate educational programs. This surprised me. Is the inherent and realistic danger too frightening to even be openly considered? As aware as we may think our self, does denial quickly close over in order for us to go on? Do we believe that it won't happen here and the sun will come up in the morning? One art therapist wrote:

> There is not enough emphasis on training clinicians to deal with potential hazards, especially around self defense in the event of an attack. I think there is an assumption that since clinicians are "intuitive" and know how to assess individuals they should be able to assess risk and intervene before something dangerous happens. There is a sort of pervasive "it won't happen to me" ideology that I hear from fellow clinicians.

The main intention of this book is to make art therapists aware of how unpredictable violence is in their day-to-day work with clients, and how present the potential of danger may be so that they can take all the preventive steps they can to stay safe. In this book, I have provided a look at the cultural and clinical landscape we live in and offered suggestions for help and support for art therapists in a dangerous practice and culture. Now it is up to graduate programs, mental health facilities and clinicians to pay attention and to act. The underlying question must be: Is danger so prevalent that people should decide to do something else with their life? No! Art therapy is the best work there is! Unforeseen and precipitous violence is a reality of the times we live in now, but it has always been a reality of the work we do.

A sage once wrote these rules that I have adapted. I recommend them:

1. Don't push too many rocks uphill. It can be ineffective and is definitely exhausting. Choose your battles.
2. Find a friend.
3. Stay alive.

Can violence be predicted? No. Can violence be predicted by interpreting violent imagery in artwork? No. Can violence be predicted from art therapy imagery by a skillful and experienced art therapist? No. And the final question: Is a mass murderer mentally ill? This week there were 14 bombs mailed to Democratic political figures. The bomber was apprehended and found to be a White Supremacist and a conspiracy theorist. Talking Heads on news programs called him mentally ill. Was he? Maybe. However, being a White supremacist and a conspiracy theorist are not diagnosable pathologies. What can *you* do? Stay safe yourself and become an advocate for safety in your school and workplace.

Addendum:

October 10, 2018: It has been confirmed that a mass shooter killed 11 people, ages 54-97 inside a synagogue in Pittsburgh, during Saturday Shabot services. One killed was a Holocaust survivor. As the shooter walked in he shouted "All Jews must die." He carried an assault rifle and three revolvers. Others were wounded also including six policemen. The shooter was wounded and taken into custody. This was the most violent assault on Jews in United States history. The Anti-Defamation League reported that anti-semitism was up 57 percent in 2018.

REFERENCES

Alaszewski, A., Harrison, L., & Manthorpe, J. (Eds.). (1998). *Risk, health and welfare: Policies, strategies and practice.* Buckingham, U.K: Open University Press.

American Psychiatric Association, Fourth edition. (1994). *Diagnostic and statistical manual of mental disorders.* Washington, D.C.: American Psychiatric Association.

American Psychiatric Association, Fifth edition. (2013). *Diagnostic and statistical manual of mental disorders.* Washington, D.C.: American Psychiatric Association.

April 2, 2018. Gun control and fall elections: Moment or movement? The New York Times, p. A1.

Ashton-Warner, S. (1986, First published in 1963). *Teacher.* New York: Simon & Schuster.

Corrigan, P. & Watson, A. (2002). Understanding the impact of stigma on people with mental illness. *World Psychiatry, 1*(1) February, pp. 16–20.

Elledge, J. (2013). *Henry Darger: Throwaway boy, the tragic life of an outsider artist.* New York and UK: Overlook Duckworth, Peter Mayer Publishers, Inc.

Espinosa, V. (2015). *Martin Ramirez, framing his life and art.* Austin, Texas: University of Texas Press.

Frank, P. (2015). Feminist artist explains her morbid obsession with serial killers. https: www.huffingtonpost.com/entry/feminist-artist-explains-her-morbid-fascination-with-serial-killers. Retrieved 6/15/2018.

Friedman, M. (2014). The stigma of mental illness is making us sicker. https://www.psychologytoday.com/blog/brick-brick/201405/the-stigma-mental-illness-is . . . Retrieved 2/19/2018.

Friedman, T. (2016). *Thank you for being late.* New York: Farrar, Straus and Giroux.

Fuller Torrey, E. (2014). *American psychosis: How the federal government destroyed the mental illness treatment system.* Oxford and New York: Oxford University Press.

Graeber, D. (2018). *Bullshit jobs.* New York: Simon & Schuster.

Gussak, D. (2013). *Art on trial, art therapy in capital murder cases.* New York: Columbia University Press.

Junge, M. (2010). *The modern history of art therapy.* Springfield, IL: Charles C Thomas.

Klarevas, L. (2016). *Rampage shooting: Securing America from mass shootings.* Amherst, New York: Prometheus Books.

Ladd, C. (October 6, 2017). Ten lies distort the gun control debate. *Forbes.* https://www.forbes.com/sites/chrisladd/2017/10/06/ten-lies-distort-the-gun - control-debate/ Retrieved 8/7/2016.

March 25, 2018.With passion and fury, students march on guns. *The New York Times,* p. A1.

MacGregor, J. (1989). *The discovery of the art of the insane.* Princeton, New Jersey: Princeton University Press.

Pope, K., & Vasquez, M. (2016). *Ethics in psychotherapy and counseling: A practical guide, 5th Edition.* New York: Wiley.

Redfield Jamison, K. (1994). *Touched with fire: Manic-depressive illness and the artistic temperament.* New York: Free Press Paperback, a division of Simon & Schuster.

Redfield Jamison, K. (1995). *An unquiet mind: A memoir of moods and madness.* New York: Alfred A. Knopf.

Roth, A. (2018). *Insane.* New York: Basic Books.

Salem Keizer School District. (2017). Student Threat Assessment and Management System—Level 1 Protocol.

Sandberg, D., McNiel, D., & Binder, R. (1998). Characteristics of psychiatric inpatients who stalk, threaten, or harass hospital staff after discharge. *American Journal of Psychiatry, 155*(8), pp. 1102–1105.

Sawyer, K. (posted August 6, 2006). The myth of the mentally ill artist. http://Keithsawyer.worldpress.com/2009/08/the_myth_of_the_mentally-ill-creative. Blog entry. Retrieved 4-5-2018.

Schjeldahl, P. (2002). Hitler as artist. New York: *New Yorker Magazine.*

Schug, R., & Fradella, H. (2015). *Mental illness and crime.* California and London: SAGE Publications.

Shannon, S. (2007). *Please don't label my child.* Emmaus, Pennsylvania: Rodale, Inc.

Stewart, E. (Fall 2007). "In the Realms of the Unreal: The mystery of Henry Darger." Video Review. *Art Therapy: Journal of the American Art Therapy Association, 24*(2). pp. 95–96.

Tishler, C., Gordon, L., & Landry-Meyer, L. (2000). Managing the violent patient: A guide for psychologists and other mental health professionals. *Professional Psychology: Research and Practice, 31*(1), pp. 34–41.

Traister, R. (2018). *Good and mad, the revolutionary power of women's anger.* New York: Simon & Schuster.

Vasilogambros, M. (August 2, 2018). After Parkland, states pass 50 new gun-control laws. *Huffington Post.* https://www.huffingtonpost.com/entry/parkland-shooting -gun-control-laws_us_5b630dd8e4. Retrieved 8/7/2018.

Warburton, K., & Stahl, S. (Eds.). (2016). *Violence and psychiatry.* Cambridge, U.K: Cambridge University Press.

Wedge, M. (2011). Six problems with psychiatric diagnosis for children. *Suffer the children.* https://www.psychologytoday.com/blog/suffer_the_children./201/05 /six-problems . . . Retrieved 2-19-2018.

Wilson, L. (Ed.). (2017). *The Wiley handbook of the psychology of mass shootings.* Chichester, West Sussex, U.K.: John Wiley & Sons, Inc.

Whitaker, R. (2002, 2010 Edition). *Mad in America.* New York: Basic Books.

Yu, J. (2093). "In the realms of the unreal: The mystery of Henry Darger." DVD. Produced by Diorama Films. LLC for the Independent Television Service with funding provided by the Corporation for Public Broadcasting. Distributed by Wellspring Media.

ABOUT THE AUTHOR

Maxine Borowsky Junge was born in Los Angeles and lived there until 18 years ago when she moved to Whidbey Island, Washington after retirement from Loyola Marymount University where she was faculty member and Chair of the Marital and Family Therapy/Clinical Art Therapy Department. She is now Professor Emerita. She earned a B.A. in Art and Humanities from Scripps College, an M.S.W. from the University of Southern California and a Ph.D. in Human and Organizational Systems from Fielding Graduate University. She is a visual artist with professional art training since the age of 12, including M.F.A.education at UCLA.

Dr. Junge is known as a pioneer in the art therapy profession, formally beginning her art therapy career in 1973 with an apprenticeship with Helen Landgarten, an art therapy visionary. She began teaching art therapy in 1974 in Landgarten's Clinical Art Therapy program at Immaculate Heart College in Hollywood, California which was the first art therapy program in the United States west of the Mississippi River. With Helen, she helped grow the program there, including a focus on job development for art therapists in the greater Los Angeles area. She continued developing the program when it moved in 1980 to Loyola Marymount University and later became Chair. She is long-time art psychotherapist and maintained a private practice in Los Angeles for many decades.

Since moving to Whidbey Island, she has taught at Goddard College in Vermont, Antioch University in Seattle, and has continued to teach, consult, supervise and train many art therapy students and practitioners and psychotherapists of all kinds. Her 1994 book, *A History of Art Therapy in the United States* was the first inclusive history in book form of this innovative profession. It was published by the American Art Therapy Association on its 25th anniversary. In 2010, *The Modern History of Art Therapy in the United States* was published. It is taught in art therapy graduate programs across the country. Her other books include *Architects of Art Therapy: Memoirs and Life Stories; Creative Realities: The Search for Meanings; Mourning, Memory and Life Itself, Essays by an Art Therapist; Graphic Facilitation and Art Therapy: Imagery and Metaphor in Organizational Development; Identity in Art Therapy: Personal and*

133

Professional Perspectives and *Becoming an Art Therapist.* Dr. Junge's most recent book, Dear Myra, *Dear Max, A Conversation About Aging* was co-authored with Myra Levick, a founder of art therapy and AATA's first President. Dr. Junge has contributed many chapters and articles on art therapy to books and journals and has given presentations nationally and internationally.

Dr. Junge has been actively involved in the mental health system since 1971 and has observed firsthand it's ebbs and flows since then.

CHARLES C THOMAS • PUBLISHER, LTD.